Milton and Anna Grass

Stockings for a Queen

The Life of the Rev. William Lee,
the Elizabethan Inventor

HEINEMANN : LONDON

William Heinemann Ltd

LONDON   MELBOURNE   TORONTC

CAPE TOWN   AUCKLAND

MADE AND PRINTED IN GREAT BRITAIN BY
MORRISON AND GIBB LIMITED, LONDON AND EDINBURGH

FOREWORD

Mankind owes perhaps as much to the genius of the inventor, the Rev. William Lee, as to that of his famous contemporary William Shakespeare. The dramatist's plays have come down to us through the centuries, most of them in their original form, even in the very words and sentences of the author, but the notes and drawings of the engineer have disappeared. Not one of his sketches has survived. Only his ingenious idea has lived on, an idea so potent that it has multiplied ten-thousandfold. From the seed that held the vital ingredients has grown not one mighty tree but a whole forest. Lee's basic principle of machine knitting laid the foundation for world industries. It is a fascinating story.

In the twelfth century, Cistercian monks had come from France, set up large sheep farms and organized wool growing in the British Isles. Two hundred monasteries were thus engaged in 1300. At first they sold their crops locally, later they made deals with export merchants and buyers overseas. Abbots and Priors were keen businessmen who anticipated modern commercial practice by entering into long-term contracts. When Henry VIII broke away from Rome in 1538, he confiscated all church property and the wool trade of the monks passed into private hands, favourites of the king and wealthy merchants who could pay for the privileges. Half the nation was occupied with wool. Apart from spinners, weavers and dyers, there were thousands of hand-knitters in the West of England, East Anglia, Lincolnshire and the Yorkshire Dales using the rivers to transport their knitted caps and stockings to the market towns and the ports from where they were shipped abroad.

Then in 1589 Lee invented the stocking frame. It was the most important event in the whole history of knitting. Tradition has it that he courted a young woman who was too preoccupied with knitting to find enough time for her impatient suitor. Watching her nimble fingers looping thread into row after row of uniform stitches, he conceived the idea of constructing a machine which would imitate the movement of the needles. The task completed he demonstrated his knitting machine to the Queen and asked her for a patent, but she refused to grant it, fearing it might endanger the livelihood of her hand-knitters. 'Make an engine that knits stockings of silk instead of wool', she demanded. Lee went away and within some eight years, achieved the seemingly impossible. He built a machine with finer needles and could now knit silk stockings without, however, securing the patent he had hoped for. The disillusioned inventor emigrated to France and set up a workshop in Rouen, but misfortune followed him and he died in 1610 an unknown stranger in a foreign land.

The story of William Lee has been told many times these past 300 years. Unfortunately we have no contemporary record of it, apart from a cryptic sentence or two by early historians such as Stow. No doubt the importance of the invention was not recognized at first and those who practised the mystery, the framework knitters as they called themselves, had reason to keep quiet about it. Apart from a handwritten petition to Oliver Cromwell asking for a charter, the tale seems to have been passed on by word of mouth. Only in the eighteenth century did historians and antiquarians become sufficiently interested to write about William Lee and his wonderful machine. Some copied inaccurately, others varied the story according to their imagination or personal approach, adding the results of their own researches. Most detailed evidence has been lost for ever, but who knows what information may still lie hidden in forgotten old documents, waiting to be discovered? It is this intriguing thought which has stirred each generation of writers and historians to probe afresh, endeavouring to fill in some more of the all-too-sketchy picture we have of this great Elizabethan engineer and inventor, his circumstances and surroundings.

In their searches, Mr. and Mrs. Grass of New Canaan, Connecticut, have found much about Lee that is new. Their vivid description of the inventor's youth and the years he spent at Cambridge, the interesting background of university life and influence, make absorbing reading, but the most exciting part of this unusual book is undoubtedly the contract of February 10, 1611, made between William Lee and Pierre de Caux.

Many writers have told us about the efforts made by Henry IV to develop the silk industry in the North of France, and that Lee accepted the invitation of Sully, duke of Rosny, and emigrated with his knitting machines to Rouen, but none was able to prove the truth of this tale. Each author copied it in good faith from the one before him. I tried for years to find some documentary evidence, visited Rouen twice and even offered a reward of 100 guineas for any proof of our hero's presence in France, but all in vain. Partly by hard, methodical work, partly by good fortune which every successful researcher needs in rich measure, Mr. and Mrs. Grass have unearthed the elusive information. It is a most welcome and important discovery which, in itself, amply justifies this book. I wish the volume and its authors every success.

E. W. Pasold

CONTENTS

ix

TO OUR GRANDCHILDREN

In the promise of the future,
Discovery in the uses of the past.

'D'un art toujours ançien,
'D'un art toujours nouveau
'Qui m'expliquera le prodige?'

—M. Heddé, *Histoire de L'Invention des Métiers
de Bas.* Académie de Nîmes, Procès-
Verbaux, 6 Mars 1852.

PHOTOGRAPHIC PLATES

Front endpaper: Visit of Queen Elizabeth I to
Blackfriars, 15 June 1600. Attributed to
Marcus Gheeraerts.

Back endpaper: Christ's College, Cambridge, in
the seventeenth century.

ACKNOWLEDGEMENTS OF PLATES

Acknowledgements are due to the following for permission
to reproduce the plates indicated:
The Trustees of the British Museum—plates 1 and 17;
University Archives, Old Schools, Cambridge—plate 2;
Christ's College Library, Cambridge—plate 3; The Victoria
and Albert Museum, London—plate 5; from Seligman
Hughes book, *Domestic Needlework*—plate 6; The Marquis
of Salisbury—plate 8; Col. N. V. Stopford-Sackville and the
National Portrait Gallery, London—plate 9; Christ's
College, University of Cambridge—plate 10; National
Portrait Gallery, London—plates 11 and 12; Hispanic
Society, New York City—plate 13; Guildhall Library,
London—plate 14; Leicester Museum and Art Gallery—
plate 15; Archives de la Seine Maritime, Rouen, France—
plate 16.
The front endpaper is from a painting at Sherbourne
Castle, and the back endpaper is reproduced by permission
of The Folger Shakespeare Library, Washington, D.C.

ACKNOWLEDGEMENTS

First in the record of the debts we owe in this endeavour to tell a story of 400 years ago is that to our local New Canaan Library. To Mrs. Constance Collins, Director, and her staff goes our gratitude for personal interest in providing a quiet workroom; meeting requests for special books; and for their time in expediting inter-library service for books from both sides of the Atlantic. In turn, credits are due to La Bibliothèque du Conservatoire National des Arts et Métiers, Paris; and to Mrs. Lamon Coons, Reference Librarian, Yale University, for co-operative interest and sending of the requisite volumes.

In quest of knowledge of the beginnings of the life story of the Rev. William Lee we are grateful for the benefits afforded us in his native Nottinghamshire: to the Rev. Thomas Hoyle for the conscientious perusals of his four-century heritage of records of St. Wilfrid's Church Parish and for other information pertaining to Calverton, then and now; to Mrs. Hoyle for her attendant interest and warm hospitality extended to us in the Calverton Vicarage; to the Rev. James Foxcroft for checking the early registers of St. Swithin's Church, Woodborough.

In neighbouring Nottingham our indebtedness is due to Mrs. Longworthy, Reference Librarian of the Public Library, in making accessible files of material for our particular interest and acquainting us with other relevant local resources. The Mechanics Institute Library, the Bromley Library housing the Thoroton Transactions, the City of Nottingham Museum and

Art Gallery, all added dimension to our opportunities for research.

In our search for family documents the aid of Mr. W. R. Serjeant of the County Records Office was marked by patience and understanding with profit to us for his interpretation of local features in the disclosed documents. Our debt to Professor Jonathan D. Chambers, Department of Economic History, University of Nottingham, is not only for his long-standing interest through communications and conferences in Nottingham but especially for his first encouragement to us to pursue our endeavour, thus 'to clear the many mysteries about the curate William Lee who brought off such an amazing achievement in a lonely parsonage'.

At Cambridge, grateful acknowledgement is due to Dr. A. L. Peck, Librarian, Christ's College, and to Mrs. Audrey Beatty, Sub-Librarian, who gave us unstintingly of their time and knowledge helpful to our preparation of a bibliography relating to the Cambridge of the Divinity student William Lee. To Miss E. Peek, Keeper of the University Archives, the Old Schools, Cambridge, our thanks are also due.

It was a fruitful search that Mr. Chandler of the Corporation of London, Guildhall, helped us to accomplish in referring us to a pertinent document. For the facilities of the Guildhall Library, the British Museum Reading and Manuscript Rooms, the Public Records Office, the Goldsmiths' Library, University of London, and the National Portrait Gallery, we offer our appreciation and, on the other side of the Atlantic, to the New York Public Library, the French Institute, New York, and to the Ferguson Library, Stamford, Connecticut, for their co-operation.

To the Folger Shakespeare Library, Washington, D.C., we are indebted for its unique facilities for research and also, invaluable for us, its comprehensive range of books of the Tudor period. Indeed, our special thanks are due to Dr. Louis B. Wright, Director, for the conference time he accorded us.

In our need to clear many questions we were privileged in communications, in writing or in conferences, with Mr. Claude Blair, Department of Metalwork, Victoria and Albert Museum, London; Mr. R. M. Beaumont, Honorary Librarian, Southwell Minster, Nottingham; Curator E. J. Daws, City of Nottingham Museum and Art Gallery; W. L. Margetson, President Allen Solly & Co. Ltd.; Miss F. Knowles, Librarian, Regional College of Technology, Nottingham; Mr. J. W. Goodison, Deputy Director, Fitzwilliam Museum, Cambridge; Mr. K. R. Gilbert, Director, Science Museum, London; Annette Fern, Librarian, University of Chicago; David Finch, Director, French Institute, New York; Elizabeth Hammond Taylor, Hammond Museum, Westchester, New York; Hon. Sec. Miss Irene Scouloudi, The Huguenot Society of London; and to Lord Salisbury, Hatfield House, Hertfordshire, where Queen Elizabeth I's silk stockings are on view.

In France, our gratitude to Mme. Dupic, Directrice, Bibliothèque Municipale, Rouen, for her perceptive understanding of our quest in making available relevant books from the Bibliothèque Nationale, Paris, and for arranging our introduction to the Archivist des Services de la Seine Maritime, M. André le Roi, who in turn expedited our search for a long undisclosed document. Our appreciation also is due to M. Gerard Namer, Bibliothécaire, for the time and critical acumen he brought to the transcription and translation of this early seventeenth-century trade agreement. To the Archivists des Services Departmentales, M. Dousset and M. Burckard, our grateful acknowledgement is extended for their searches over several years in answer to our questions relating to data drawn from archival source materials and for sending us pertinent publications of the Commission des Antiquités de la Seine Inférieure. To meet a further need of transcription of an undeciphered portion of the original document, the De Caux-Lee contract, our thanks go to Yale University's Professors Howard Carey and Eric Hicks for their gracious attention and counsel; to the École Nationale des Chartes, Paris, for its transcription to modern French; and to Professor Hicks and to Mrs. Thérèse Hicks for its English translation.

We owe to Mr. Claude Blair, Victoria and Albert Museum, London, our meeting with Mr. Eric Walter Pasold, O.B.E., Chairman, Pasolds Ltd. We are deeply appreciative of the encouragement and inspiration we have received from Mr. Pasold, whose sustained interest in the textiles field derives from nine generations of family activity. His creativity is witnessed in his founding of the Pasold Research Fund for the promotion of research into economic, social and natural history. For his confidence in us to tell the story of 'our common hero', the inventor of the knitting loom, and reflected in the expression of the Fund, we are grateful.

To Mr. John St. John, of the staff of the publisher, William Heinemann Ltd. of London, our especial thanks are due for his responsive understanding of our endeavour and in its course of handling of many details, reaching across the sea, from manuscript to book completion.

New Canaan,   Milton N. Grass
Connecticut   Anna M. Grass

Bunhill Row

1. Map of London by Richard Newcourt (1658) showing Bunhill Row.

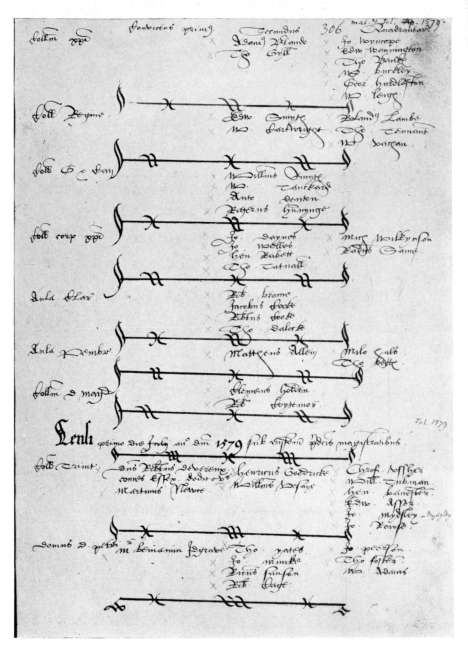

2. Record of William Lee's matriculation at Christ's College. 'W. Leige' is the sixth name from the top.

'One Ring of Gold'

In praising a noble personage, and in setting forth at large
his worthiness, one should observe three things . . . before
his life, in his life, and after his death . . .[1]

So wrote Quintillian, the Roman rhetorician and critic, in
the first century B.C. and his injunctions are not inappropriate
to tracing the life and times of William Lee, the inventor of
the knitting loom.

The place and exact date of Lee's birth cannot be authen-
ticated by the parish records of either St. Wilfrid's in
Calverton, or St. Swithin's in Woodborough, the two villages
which have claimed and were credited at one time or another
with that honour.

Before the reign of Queen Elizabeth the registration of
births and deaths was less than perfect and vital statistics
of the period are either missing or incomplete. In Nottinghamshire over the centuries . . . 'it will be found old names
continuously disappear, while new ones occur, themselves
in turn vanishing'.[2]

Thoroton, the historian of Nottinghamshire, wrote about
the birthplace of Lee: 'In Calverton was born William Lee
. . . Master of Arts in Cambridge.' His *Antiquities of
Nottinghamshire*, written in 1677, was compiled at a time
when he was able to secure authentic information from
individuals, who either themselves or through members

[1] Quoted by Thomas Wilson: *The Art of Rhetoric* (1560).
[2] S. A. Peyton: *The Village Population in the Tudor Lay Subsidy Rolls*
(1915).

of their family, could have had personal contact with or knowledge of the inventor.[3]

The Parish Register of St. Swithin's Church of Woodborough, on the other hand, does not establish the date of his birth, nor that he was born in that village. Those writers who assert he was born there wrote at a much later date. They make the claim but with no more positive or substantiating evidence than 'it was said'.[4]

By contrast, in substantiation that William Lee the inventor was born in Calverton rather than Woodborough, there is the positive affirmation in the Petition of the Frame-Work Knitters Guild to the Protector, Oliver Cromwell, in 1657: 'The trade of frame-work knitting was invented and found out by one William Lee, of *Calverton*, in the County of Nottingham.'

This should be acceptable documentation that Calverton was his birthplace since the petition was presented at a time when 'everything must have been fresh in the memory of those by whom it was presented: every circumstance could be easily examined, and the petitioners must have realized that any misrepresentation could be easily contradicted'.[5]

Birth dates were not recorded in St. Wilfrid's at Calverton prior to 1578 so no actual entry is found in the parish register for the inventor.[6] His birth date may be approximated perhaps by taking as a basis the date of his matriculation at Christ's College, Cambridge, in May 1579.[7] If it is

---

[3] Robert Thoroton: *Antiquities of Nottinghamshire* (1677), printed by Robert White, at the Sign of the Phoenix, in St. Paul's Churchyard. In a copy in the Bromley House Library, Nottingham, there is a notation, '*Ex relatione Johanis Story*', as being the source of the information but it is not stated who Johanis Story was.

[4] Deering wrote *Nottingham Vetus et Nova* in 1751; Blackner wrote his *History of Nottingham* in 1815; Cooper his *Athenae Cantabrigensis* in 1840; Rev. Walter Buckland wrote his *History of Woodborough* in 1897.

[5] Johan Beckmann: *History of Inventions* (1789).

[6] St. Wilfrid Parish Registers, Calverton: Rev. T. O. Hoyle, Vicar (1964).

[7] The Grace Books, Archives of Cambridge University. In the Grace Books, which are Registries of the Old Schools, were entered 'all certificates of record'.

assumed that he was fifteen years old, which was an average age of matriculation at that time, then his birth date would be 1564. If twenty years old is taken, then the year of his birth would be 1559.[8] The actual date might be some year in between.

Adding to the confusion of the genealogy of the Lee family, in the Calverton parish register there are two entries of the death of 'the wife of William Lee'. One entry is for 'Anne, the wife of William Lee . . . buried Jan. 1589–90'. The other for 'Paula the wife of William Lee . . . buried in 1591'. Since there is no factual evidence of the marriage of the inventor, there is the possibility that one of these women could have been his mother, the other his grandmother.

Unfortunately, letters, diaries, or personal memoranda have not survived. However, now brought to light among other documents are two wills which help to establish Lee's 'realm, town, parents, and ancestors':[9]

> The will of Margaret Oliver, of Calverton, widow, dated Jan. 4, 1565, bequeathing 'to William Lee my son-in-law . . . the ox-gang of my corn remaining on the ground' . . . and to 'William Lee the younger, . . . one ewe and one lamb'.[10]
> The will and probate of 'William Lee Yeoman' of Calverton, dated April 16, 1607 . . . bequeathing to . . . 'my eldest son . . . William Lee . . . one ring of gold'.[11]

Further adding to the confusion are the entries in St. Wilfrid's Register of the deaths of two William Lees, one recorded in 1595, the other in 1607. Neither was William Lee the inventor.

[8] G. M. Trevelyan: *English Social History* (1944). When Erasmus was at Cambridge, there were more students aged seventeen, and fewer aged fourteen, than before the beginning of the sixteenth century.
[9] Quoted by Wilson: op. cit.
[10] The will of Margaret Oliver, Calverton, Jan. 4, 1565. Southwell Wills. DD PRSW. County Records Office. Nottingham.
[11] The Will and Probate of William Lee, Yeoman, April 16, 1607. DD PRSW. County Records Office. Nottingham.

The 'William Lee the Elder' referred to in the Register as 'buried the first day of March, 1595' is the William Lee referred to in the will of Margaret Oliver as 'William Lee the older', and as 'William Lee . . . my son-in-law'. He was the grandfather of the inventor and had married the daughter of William Oliver, a vicar in Calverton, as early as 1535.[12]

The William Lee referred to in Margaret Oliver's will as 'William Lee the Younger' was the father of the inventor and was the recipient under her will of 'one ewe and one lamb'. Significantly, forty-two years later, in his own will he made the same bequest '. . . to every one of my children's children, who shall be alive at my decease . . . one ewe sheep, of one year old at the least'. He died on April 16, 1607, describing himself in this same will as a 'yeoman' and directing 'to be buried in the church or churchyard of Calverton'. As he commended his soul to Almighty God, he further ordered that 'seven shillings be bestowed yearly towards increasing of the poor man's stock'.

The inventor's father had a family of nine children, four girls and five boys, including the inventor. Entered in St. Wilfrid's Register are the names of Edward born 1574, Robert 1577, John 1580. James the youngest, born in 1582, is said to have sympathized with what were then considered the revolutionary ideas of his brother William, as will be seen later.

In his will probated in 1607, Lee's father significantly made no provision for James the youngest, whose confidence in his brother's invention was to prove unfailing. Bequests of a minor character were made to the daughters and to John the second-born. Almost the entire estate was bequeathed to Edward, the fourth son. To John he left:

> That house and tenement in Calverton, wherein I now dwell, with all . . . the lands, measures, closures, commodities and emoluments whatsoever, with the appurtenances thereto belonging . . .

[12] *The Eagle*, St. John's College, Vol. 15 (1889).

One parcel of land called 'Thorndall', within the Parish of Calverton, and in the King's Book . . . 8 acres thereabouts . . .
Another parcel of ground within the Parish of Oxton, called the Myrie (Muddy) Meadow . . .

To Edward was bequeathed:

The reversion of a lease, possessed in Morwood, in the County of Darby. Also . . . all my goods, moveable and immoveable, which should happen to be in Morwood.

Then:

I do ordain and make my two sons, Edward and John, the full executors of this, my last will and testament, and to whom I give the residue of all my goods, to be equally divided between them.

To his eldest son, William, who left home, hearth, and church to pursue an inventor's vision, he bequeathed:

Item. I give to my oldest son, William, one ring of gold, in the value worth 20 shillings, in full discharge of his filial portion.[13]

'One ring of gold . . . in full discharge . . .' By contrast he bequeathed to one of his daughters, Isabell, 'Forty shillings . . . for and in the name of a child's part or customary portion'.

By disinheriting William, for that is what it amounted to, he cut completely across the laws of primogeniture, the ancient custom prevailing in England since Norman times of bequeathing to the eldest son all the real property. Was

[13] In the Elizabethan era, the gift of a ring was to close friends (rather than to kin like an eldest son), a mark of affection. William Shakespeare made a bequest in his will to four of his brother actors and partners: 'To my fellowes . . . 26/8 a piece . . . to buy them rings' (Source, G. F. Bentley, *Shakespeare and His Theatre*).

the yeoman-father showing his bitter disappointment in an eldest son determined to follow a calling other than the church?

Nor did his decisions in the legacy manifest other aspects of a yeoman-parent, as described by the historian, Harrison:

> ... Yeomen ... do come to great wealth, inasmuch as many of them are able, and do buie the lands of unthriftie gentlemen ... and after setting their sonnes to schooles, to the universities, and to the Innes ... or otherwise leaving them sufficient lands.[14]

If it were the ambition of a yeoman to have a son in the church, he might have considered that the church offered great opportunities for a son not born of the nobility or gentry. Such a son, trained for Holy Orders at Oxford or Cambridge, would be a person of standing and do a great good both in the world and in his parish as a Curate. So perhaps were the ambitious thoughts of the yeoman who displayed modesty, paid his debts, and practised good husbandry.[15]

Ironically, Lee's father did not realize that it would be at the very university itself, in the course of actually training for a spiritual calling, that his son would experience a change towards a temporal calling. He did not perceive that the 'new' philosophies of Luther, and that expounded by Erasmus and the preachers at Cambridge, would influence his son in changing the interpretation of the 'opportunity to serve God'.[16]

At the time he wrote his will, did he perhaps ponder the words of that great cynic, Machiavelli? 'A son may bear with equanimity the loss of his father, but the loss of his inheritance may drive him to despair.'[17]

---

[14] Rev. William Harrison: *Description of The Island of Great Britain* 2nd Edition (1587).
[15] P. H. Ditchfield: *The Old-Time Parson* (1905).
[16] William Perkins: *A Treatise of the Vocations* (1603).
[17] Nicolo Machiavelli: *The Prince* (1500).

Turning from this survey of Lee's antecedents it is possible to reconstruct the actual times in which he lived as a boy, and the impressions which shaped his mind, from a number of historical sources.

Calverton itself, seven miles north of Nottingham, one mile south of Woodborough, 'where calves are kept', was certified in the Domesday Book of 1065 as 'having a church, a priest and two acres of pasture-land and pasture-wood'. It nestled in the heart of the Midlands in the south-west corner of Sherwood Forest.[18] At the beginning of the later half of the sixteenth century when William Lee was born, it had grown to be a pleasant Tudor village of about 100 homes, the inhabitants being engaged in husbandry, sheep-grazing, or dairy-farming.

Much of Sherwood Forest was cut down, although there were still signs of its ancient majesty in the sturdy oak trees that lined the dirt road in front of St. Wilfrid's Church. On a clear day in the far distance could be seen the Cotswold Hills, with London about 125 miles away.

In his *Sad Shepherd, or a Tale of Robin Hood*, Ben Johnson wrote:

> ... *Odd tales of an outlaw, Robin Hood,*
> *that revelled here in Sherwood.*

The inhabitants of Nottinghamshire still dreamed fondly of the past and so no doubt did young William. At archery competitions the village marksmen, dressed in costumes of Robin Hood and Little John, led the village procession to the butts; shooting at the butts was encouraged by proclamation to preserve England's military monopoly with the long bow.[19] Certainly to some in Nottinghamshire, non-observance of laws came naturally, as is shown by a Presentment in the Constable Enquests, dated April 25, 1547:

[18] Thoroton: op. cit.

[19] Trevelyan op. cit.: 'The long bow continued to be exalted as the national weapon of defence until 1595, when the arquebus and the musket became the national weapons of defence.'

'Maister Haisylryg, John Cowper and Edward Edmonson, for selling wine above the price of Master Mayor's commandment . . . and . . . William Lovett . . . for keeping unlawful games at his house.'[20]

In the Presentments of April 30, 1556, there is actually a charge against a certain 'Lee' who may very well have been a relative of the inventor's family: 'We do pryssent Tomas Lees, because he doth sell all (ale) being not alloud (not licensed).'

And there is a further entry in the Chamberlain's 'Records of the Borough' of another person who was to have a vital influence on the life of the inventor: 'Item: Given to Lord Hunsdon, the 24th of Auguste, 1572, two gallands (gallons) of wyne (wine), and one pound of sewgar (sugar).'[21]

None could have guessed how this mighty and this low-born life were to run together. At that time Lord Hunsdon was the Lord Warden of the East Marches of Scotland and Governor of Berwick. What official duties he performed or was expected to perform, entitling him to 'presentes and rewards' from the Borough of Nottingham, are not recorded though it is known that August 24 was the day of gratuities for the Elizabethan Court favourites.

The parcel of land called ThornDall belonging to Yeoman William Lee was an 'assorte' or clearing in the forest for which 6 pence yearly was paid to the King. The family parcel in the parish of Oxton was called the 'Muddy Meadow'. Both were located in the countryside where:

> The air is good, wholesome and delectable. The soil is rich, sandy and clair. Surely, for corn and grass so fruitful that secondeth any in the realm, and for water, woods and canal coals abundantly stored.[22]

In this lush environment young William Lee and his

---

[20] Records of the Town of Nottingham. Reprinted by the City.
[21] Extracts from the Chamberlain's Accounts, Borough of Nottingham.
[22] John Speed: *Atlas of England and Wales* (1677).

brothers Edward and John will have walked along the banks of the stream called the River Dover-Bets, which feeds into the River Leen and the River Trent. Their mouths may even have been filled with Neward-Worksop licorice '. . . very delicious and good and grown in the fields' not far from their home.

Perhaps it was one of those rare days when the boys had a holiday from school and had ridden into Nottingham on top of one of their father's large wains, when he hauled a load of sacks of wool to be sold to the wholesale dealers in the market-place of the town. The name *Nottingham* means literally 'the dwelling of caves' for from time immemorial caves have existed on its hillsides, hewed out of the rock, complete with chimneys, stairways, and windows. In ancient times these caves were used for dwellings but in the sixteenth century they were turned to baser uses.[23]

Smugglers were said to frequent them and when dusk fell young William may have imagined he discerned in the shadows their outlines, for they used the caves as hiding places, storing deep in the caverns the bags of wool on which the government at various times placed duties and embargoes, and forbade exportation. On a dark night the smugglers carried the bags down to the river boats which silently slipped past the customs officers, sailing to Hull, where the wool was transhipped on to Channel boats, and sold to the Low Countries.

To keen-eyed William, as interesting as the caves were the sights he saw as he walked along the banks of the Trent, at that time considered one of the four great rivers of England. With the river boats moored to the docks he could fondly touch the very bags and sacks of wool his father had sold that day to the wool dealers.

The wool, so aptly called 'golden fleeces' because of its high value, was soft and silky; the small sheep, pastured on land which at one time had been part of Sherwood Forest,

[23] William Camden: *Britannia, or a Chronological Description of Britain* (1627).

produced wool the equal in fineness of any grown in Europe.

Coal from the Nottingham area was another commodity which was shipped by the river boats to towns and villages in the Lower Valley, while lead, timber, corn, hops, and flax were piled high on the docks, waiting to be loaded on the decks and into the holds of the boats that transported them.[24] The Trent was navigable in its entirety, up from the sea to Nottingham. From Hull to Gainsborough the deeper bottoms were used, and from Gainsborough to Nottingham shallower vessels transported the cargoes.[25]

The lad William Lee no doubt looked with longing eyes as the sailors untied the ropes, cast off and sailed, catching the winds as best they could. He will have asked many questions—about the strange new worlds they sailed to, Spanish treasure ships . . . Perhaps he asked about London and the Court, about the well-beloved Queen 'Glorianna, the greatest, glorious Queene in Fairieland . . .' Little can he have dreamed that one day the two would meet.

And what may have thrilled him most perhaps was the story of another local boy, another native of Nottingham-shire—Captain Martin Frobisher, who was born and raised in nearby Finningley and who was sent by the Queen on three expeditions to the frozen Arctic seas to find a North-west Passage to China and India.[26]

William Lee and his brothers no doubt helped their family by providing food. Boys love to fish, and fish were important food. In describing the River Trent, Camden the Archaeo-logist quotes an old saying:

Lympidia Sylva focum,
Trigina dat mihil piscen.

---

[24] A. C. Wood: *History of Trade and Transport on the River Trent.* Thoroton Society. *Annals of Nottingham.* Vol. LIV. (1950).

[25] The Anonymous Historian of Nottingham: Thoroton Society. *Annals.* Vol. II (1898).

[26] Richard Hakluyt: *The English Voyages* (1583).

Sherwood my fuel,
Trent, my fish supplied.[27]

The River Leen, as well as the Trent, was still well stocked
with a great variety of fish, a welcome addition to the larder
of the Lee family on the many Holy Days when meat was
forbidden. The fishermen on the Leen, who made fishing
their sole occupation, were the favourites of the government
because they helped to man the mercantile and royal navies.[28]
Laws had been passed ordering the observance of additional
'fish days'. In 1548 Parliament designated Fridays and
Saturdays as additional fish-days; in 1563 Wednesdays were
added. Now, with three fish-days, Lent, and Ember days,[29]
William Lee's family lived under a dietary regime in which
half the year consisted of fish-days. It was expressly stated
that the purpose of these laws was political, not religious;
they were intended to maintain the sea-going population and
to limit the too great consumption of beef which could result,
through enclosures, in further opposition to the policy of
converting arable land to pasture.

As he grew older, William will have learned how to work
the weaving loom. In the inventory of his father's estate,
listing the contents of one of the chambers, there is the item:
'Yarn, wool, tow and hempine, To the value of 36s. 8d.'[30]
In this chamber, the future inventor as a child probably
observed his mother or sisters with a distaff crooked in the
elbow, spinning yarn from the flax and the wool. The women
spun the yarn and the men wove the cloth from which
garments were made: dresses for the women, doublets and
breeches for the men, and cut and sewn stockings for both
sexes. Every so often the clothier on his rounds through the
county would stop at the Lee household, paying the regular

[27] Camden: op. cit.
[28] Trevelyan: op. cit.
[29] Ember Days: Days set apart for fasting and prayer in each of the four
seasons of the year.
[30] Hempine = Flax.

and settled price for any surplus lengths of cloth they wished to sell.[31]

Perhaps it was upon this observation and practice in early childhood, and later his acquaintance with the new art of hand-knitting as practised by the women folk, that the inventor drew for inspiration.

When he rode into Nottingham another source of ideas will have sprung from watching iron-workers as they hammered bars of iron on their anvils in Bridle-Smith Gate or Girdle-Smith Alley, hand-forging snaffles, nails, ploughshares and even more delicate work such as pins and needles.[32] Or he might have learned from the skill of the woodturners as they shaved down the lumber to the proper length and width to make tubs, buckets, firkins, troughs, wagon-wains and even furniture for the house. The abundance of coal and iron-ore in the areas near Nottingham was an open invitation to blacksmiths and iron-workers to settle there.[33] The trees in Sherwood Forest furnished the woodturners, joiners, and carpenters with lumber unequalled by any place in the Kingdom.

When the artificers or craftsmen turned their backs, perhaps Lee touched or handled the tools and imagined what wonderful things could be made with them, the younger children parading all the while in front of the shops, playing with drums, fiddles, and guns made of elder-sticks, and carrying flags made from cloths stained with the juice of poppies . . .[34]

In the words of Thoroton: 'In Calverton was born William Lee . . . heir to a pretty freehold.' In his own will, the father of the inventor described himself as a yeoman '. . . I, William Lee . . . yeoman'. Thus the father was a 'yeoman-freeholder' and his family enjoyed a social status just below that of the

[31] E. Lipson: *The Economic History of England* Vol. I 12th Edition (1959).
[32] Deering: op. cit.
[33] Sir John Clapham: *Economic History of Britain* (1957).
[34] George A. Petty: Quoted in L. B. Wright's *Middle Class Culture in Elizabethan England* (1935).

gentry. No longer were the houses in Calverton the thatched one-room cottages of the yeoman of an earlier period . . . 'a dwelling of timber with walls formed of wattled mud'. Rather, the inventor's home was probably built of brick and stone, for at the beginning of the sixteenth century the houses of the better-off yeomen were being built of solid materials. On the floor a 'plaister' might have been spread which when dry became solid and hard . . . 'so that it seemeth to be firme stone, and is tred without any danger'. In the winter, fire-places and chimneys for burning pit-coal ('the smell whereof is very offensive') heated the rooms.[35]

According to the probate of the inventory of the estate of the inventor's father, there were five rooms on the ground floor of that house in Calverton, with a hallway containing many chests and presses, running down the centre. The five rooms consisted of a kitchen, a parlour with two bedsteads, and one chamber which was a sort of store-room in which were piled up 'farm produce, bacon and grease, tubs and scythes'. A nether-chamber 'with two servants beds therein' provided sleeping quarters for two servants, an indication of the economic status of the Lee family.[36] The coarse bolster and mattress of a century before had been replaced by 'goode feather-beds'. Pillows, which previously had been characterized as being 'meet only for children and women in childbirth' were now used in the Lee home.

Harrison, the social historian, was the one who complained:

> . . . when the walls of houses were of wattled willow, we had oaken men. But they became effeminate, with the increase of luxury.

Such a statement would not seem applicable to the Lee family; in the inventory there were no items of ostentatious display, though the tableware of pewter did indicate a high standard of taste in a yeoman's home.

[35] Speed: op. cit.
[36] Will and Probate of William Lee: op. cit.

The farm itself was well stocked and was equipped and furnished with all the necessary tools and agricultural implements. In the yard and barns were bullocks, kine, and calves, swine and pigs, horses, colts and fillies. Scattered about the hinge-houses and lean-to sheds were wagons, harrows, ploughs, yokes, horse-gear and beast-gear, and stone-trucks, in fact everything a substantial yeoman required to produce food-stuffs, wool, and take care of his flocks, herds, and animals.

The cows provided the Lee family with dairy products and meats. Vats, troughs, hair-cloth and 'all the malt' inventories at three pounds indicated that not all the wheat or barley was sold as grain-stuffs, but that beer and ale were brewed on the premises for home consumption. One hundred and forty-three sheep in the sheep-cotes and enclosures, inventoried at £42. 19s., supplied the wool.

Some idea of the size of Lee's farm in Calverton may be arrived at from the item in the Will of '4 ox-gangs of corn, one pea-stack and 2 loads of hay'.[37] An estimate of 320 acres has been made as the size of the land where the corn was planted, and 80 acres for the peas, an approximate total of 400 acres. Pasturage for the flock of 143 sheep and 28 bullocks, calves, and kine would indicate that additional acreage was necessary.

In a true inventory of all the goods and chattels, probated June 26, 1607, and signed by four appraisers, the value of the moveable goods was given as £203. 14s. and 8d. This

---

[37] We are indebted to Mr. W. R. Serjeant, County Archivist, County Records Office, Nottingham, for the following information concerning the 'ox-gang': An ox-gang was a basis for the measurement of land, and equalled a 'bovate'. A 'bovate' varied from 7 to 32 acres. In the open-field system of land-cultivation, it had equalled about 40 acres. For each ox-gang in cultivation the farmer would allow another ox-gang to lie fallow. William Lee would have allowed another ox-gang to remain fallow, for the peas he had planted. It might be conjectured that land-in-cultivation, necessary to produce 4 ox-gangs of corn, would equal 160 acres. Allowance for another 160 acres remaining fallow brings the total to 320 acres. Calculating 40 acres for the peas and 40 acres remaining fallow, another 80 acres can be added to an estimate of the size of the Lee farm.

figure does not include the value of the house and land in Calverton; the parcel of land called ThornDall; the parcel within the parish of Oxton called the Myrie Meadow; nor the reversion of the lease of the parcel in Morwood.

All in all, the estate from which William Lee the inventor was disinherited would have been indeed a very 'pretty freehold'.

TWO

Sizar at Cambridge

In William Lee's time many trade guilds provided scholar-ships, both at the university and grammar-school level. The Mercers' Company for instance had been made Governors of St. Paul's School in London and had established a grammar school in 1561, the purpose to be 'the bringing up of children in good manners and literature' . . . and 'children of all nations or countries, indefinitely were to be eligible'.

As early as 1555, Sir Thomas White had sponsored St. John's College at Oxford, which he dedicated to the Patron Saint of the Merchant Taylors' Company, 'that it might become an instrument for the learning of the Sciences, of Holy Divinity, Philosophy and Good Arts'.[1]

Many wealthy merchants, too, took pride in helping boys of promise, especially those who wanted to prepare them-selves for the study of Divinity. 'The frequency with which merchants endowed prospective preachers suggests an un-conscious subsidy which must have coloured the opinions of future ecclesiastics . . . in the shaping of religious beliefs to comply with middle-class identification with trade.'[2]

However, not everyone gave approval to education as a stepping-stone for the rise of the lower classes. In an earlier century the author of the *Vision of Piers Plowman*, William Langland, had complained 'against the use of schools for the advancement of the sons of the lowly to high places in the Church':

[1] C. M. Clode: *Early History of the Merchant Taylors* (1888).
[2] R. H. Tawney: *Religion and the Rise of Capitalism* (1926).

WILLIAM PERKINS The Learned, pious, and painfull
Preacher of Gods word, at St Andrewes in Cambridge where
He died Anno Dñi. 1602. Aged 44 yeares.
W. M. Sculp:

3. William Perkins, Catechist of Christ's College, expounded the new Puritan
theology on 'occupation' which greatly influenced the inventor.

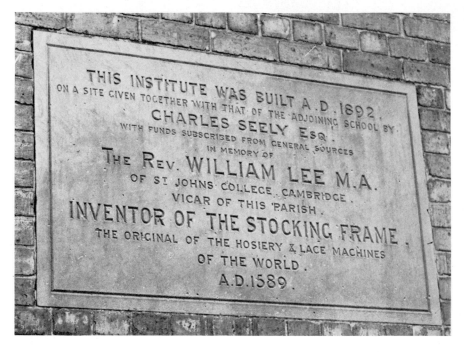

4. Memorial to William Lee: a plaque on the National School at Calverton which has since been pulled down.

Now every cobbler set his son to school,
And every beggars brat learn from the book,
And become a false Friar to serve the Devil.[3]

But the dissenting voice of Archbishop Cranmer was heard against those who would exclude the 'Plowman's Son' from the Cathedral School at Canterbury. 'Ability should be the basis of choice . . . and if the gentleman's son be apt in learning . . . let him be admitted . . . if not apt . . . let the poor man's son, being apt . . . enter his room.'[4]

At an early period in his boyhood William Lee would have understood that he would have to be proficient in many subjects, and not only in reading, writing, and good manners. His father was a devout and religious person with an abiding faith in God, writing in his Will: 'I commend my soul into the hands of Almighty God, My Master and alone Saviour, by whose precious death and blood-shedding I confidently hope to be made a partaker of his Everlasting Kingdom.' This yeoman farmer—shrewd as well as religious—realized that the way forward for his son, if God would grant, was through entering the church, like the famous Cardinal Wolsey, son of a sheep-grazier, whose sermons William Lee the Elder may have heard in St. Wilfrid's Church. Cardinal Wolsey lived in the nearby Peculiar of Southwell during the summer of 1530, about seven miles from Calverton, and preached and conducted services in the surrounding villages.[5]

Not far from Calverton, in both Nottingham and Southwell, were grammar schools which could have prepared William Lee for entrance to either Oxford or Cambridge. In Nottingham, the Free School was founded in 1554 by Agnes Mellor, the widow of a wealthy bell-founder.[6] In the Peculiar of Southwell, of which Calverton was a part, the

---

[3] W. Langland: *Piers Plowman* (circa 1400).
[4] Norman Wood: *The Reformation and English Education* (1934).
[5] Peculiar: The area in which a Chapter exercised all the powers of the Bishop of a Diocese in an Ecclesiastical Court. Source: R. M. Beaumont: *The Chapter of Southwell Minster* (1956).
[6] Records of the Borough of Nottingham.

S.Q.—C

Grammar School at Southwell Minster had a high standard for scholarship and training; in 1553 Archbishop Cranmer had written to his sister advising her 'to set her son forth to school at Southwell'.[7]

This school received special mention in one of the statutes of Elizabeth:

> In order that *pietas* for parents and benefactors . . . and those in authority and learning may flourish . . . we ordain that some man, learned in Latin and Greek, religious, honest and painstaking . . . shall be appointed to the Grammar School at Southwell, whose duty it shall be to teach, not only Latin and Greek Grammar, Latin and Greek authors, poets and orators, but also the Christian religion.[8]

The problem of school attendance would not have been difficult. William Lee's father could have provided him with a mount, or he could have boarded with a relative or friend in the village of Southwell or Nottingham. He would have studied the classics, foreign languages, some ethics and philosophy, his reading including Cato, Aesop's Fables, Ovid's *Metamorphosis*, Cicero and Horace, Tully's *Offices*, Sallus, and Greek Grammar. He would have written prose and verse compositions in Latin, being forbidden to speak any but that language during the school session, a rule enforced by the brutalities of flogging.[9]

An important duty of the master of a grammar school was teaching the young student the observance of the state religion. In her petition for the foundation of the Free School in Nottingham, Margaret Mellor had specified: 'I will and ordain that the schoolmaster, and his usher, will cause his scholars, every morning in their school-house, ere they begin

---

[7] Beaumont: op. cit.

[8] *Pietas* = Respect and reverence for those in authority. W. A. James: *An Account of the Grammar and Song-school of the Collegiate Church of Blessed Mary the Virgin of Southwell* (1927).

[9] C. Deering: *Nottingham, Vetus et Nova* (1751).

their learning every day, to recite in a high voice, the *Credo in Deum Patrem.*' The secular subjects followed after the Catechism and the Book of Common Prayer, and the student could repeat them by rote. 'The Elizabethan church and the Grammar-school provided methodical training for the memory.'[10] The trained memory was to be a major resource for Lee in the days and nights when he was to ponder on the development of his machine.

When Lee attended church he worshipped in an edifice that was ancient, even in his days. It has been told that St. Wilfrid's was rebuilt in the fourteenth century, its stones quarried in the nearby hills, and probably incorporating the foundations of an earlier Saxon structure that was first built even before William the Conqueror overcame the Saxon inhabitants.[11] As he gazed at the chapel walls, he would have noticed the sculptured stones in the lower part of the nave which, having been a band of ornamentation in the original edifice, sustained the note of antiquity.[12] The note of change was reflected in some stones of alabaster later quarried chiefly in Nottinghamshire. Their worked surfaces and excised patterns showed the various employments of the Calverton farmers during the different months and seasons of the year. They pictured the traditional husbandry, which was to be threatened later by problems of increasing wool production.

Services at St. Wilfrid's also emphasized the training he was receiving in school, 'to embrace, believe and follow the Bible in English'.[13] The priest, no longer wearing rich vestments or saying a Mass in Latin, was now a parson or a curate. Following the clerical revolution, the parish religious leader was lacking in any definite tradition and largely accepted the new doctrines as enforced by the Crown.[14]

[10] A. L. Rowse: *William Shakespeare* (1965).
[11] Deering: op. cit.
[12] Rev. T. O. Hoyle, Vicar of St. Wilfrid's Church, Calverton, 1965.
[13] G. M. Trevelyan: *English Social History* (1944).
[14] Craik and Macfarlane: *History of England* (1846).

Divinity was not yet equated with learning in the English parson as Shakespeare's description shows:

> A foolish man, an honest man, look you, and soon dash'd. He is a marvellous good neighbour, faith, a very good bowler.[15]

The university-trained curates, with the kind of mental stature that would qualify them to be more committed to their calling, were not to come until the generation after Lee.

Here at St. Wilfrid's, too, was a presage of the life that lay ahead of him, as yet quite unguessed either by his own young mind or that of his shrewdly wise father . . .

Before William Lee entered St. Wilfrid's Church on Sundays he would remove from his head and hold in his hand a 'cap of wolle-knitte'.

This cap was not worn because William Lee or his parents particularly preferred it as a style; he might have preferred one of the felt hats which had become the vogue. He wore a cap of wolle-knitte in obedience to a sumptuary law, passed by Queen Elizabeth and the Parliament in 1565:

> No person shall make, or cause to be made any cap or other thing of felt, but only hats. Nor shall they make any cap of any woollen cloth, not knitte.[16]

The law had been passed in an effort to alleviate the poor economic condition of the Cappers, a group of handicraft workers who had fallen on hard times. As early as 1520 they had complained in Chester 'their trade was decayed'. They claimed this was due to the unfair competition of the Mercers, who were dealing not only in inexpensive foreign wares but were also selling cheap caps made in other towns in England.[17] Coventry, which 'had risen by the making of cloth and caps', also complained that 'now decaying, the glory of the city decayeth'. They too had applied to Parliament for relief.

---

[15] Shakespeare: *Love's Labour's Lost.*   [16] 7. Eliz. C 11.
[17] E. Lipson: *Economic History of England* Vol. I, 12th edition (1959).

The trade of Cappers had been affected by style changes and by price competition of both foreign and domestic makers. The sumptuary law, prohibiting the *making* of any cap 'not of wolle-knitte', had been formulated to meet the threat of the group of French felt-hat makers who had migrated from Rouen, settled in the Spitalfields section of London, and then had offered keen competition by crafting 'caps of felt' in addition to 'hats of felt'.

The Act of 1565, forbidding the making of any cap not hand-knit, had not solved the problem or alleviated the distress of the cappers. The Act of 1570 followed and its preface revealed the cause and effect of the problem of 'style change':

> Great multitudes of the Queen's Majesty's subjects earning a livelihood making woollen caps were impoverished and decayed by the excessive use of hats and felts . . . and thereby divers good cities and towns are brought to desolation.

The whim of fashion had been the harbinger of distress that even Sumptuary laws could not cure.

In 1570, in response to repeated appeals the Queen again sought to meet the complaints of the Cappers by the passage of another sumptuary law:

> Every person above the age of seven years, shall wear upon the Sabbath or Holy Day (unless in the time of their travels out of town) upon their head, a cap . . . of wolle-knitte thicked and dressed in England, made within this realm, and only dressed or finished by some of the trade of cappers; upon pain to forfeit for every day not wearing 3s. 4d.: except maids, ladies and knights, Lords and other specified gentlemen of 20 marks of land.[18]

Though the base of the law had been widened at the cost of higher 'pain to forfeit', with the customary exemptions for

[18] 13. Eliz. C 19.

'Ladies and Knights' and the 'land-worthy', price competition and style competition had doomed the laws to failure; they were observed in the breach.

To our way of thinking the enactment of sumptuary laws to require the wearing or the prohibition of an article of dress in a specified manner would be considered an imposition of authority upon one's rights as an individual. However, the historian James Froude, has judged that there are two sides to the coin: 'sumptuary laws are among the exploded fallacies we smile at today, for an unwisdom which would expect to regulate private habits and manners by statute; yet, some statutes may be of moral authority, and may be regarded as an authoritative declaration of what good men considered to be right'.[19]

But whatever opinion Lee held of their rightness on that Sunday morning when he was a school-boy in Calverton on the way to service in St. Wilfrid's, his father most likely told him he would need to wear a 'cap of wolle-knitte' whether or not he liked the style. His father would remind him that, if the law were disobeyed, the penalty was 3s. 4d., a sum not to be made light of by a thrifty yeoman. Another reminder would have been that if he did not attend the church service the Lee family would be subject to an additional penalty of 12d., which the Queen had proclaimed would be levied on everyone who did not attend church on Sundays and Holy Days.

In this instrument of imposing a fine to extend the use of hand-knit caps of wool was reflected an Elizabethan economic policy to insure 'care of all my subjects', in later centuries to be known as 'full employment'. The absence-from-church fine was a means of promoting church attendance in the development of the Queen's policy to effect the alignment of church unity and the security of the realm.

So the years passed for young William Lee until one day early in May, 1579, probably in the company of several other Nottinghamshire youths who were also matriculating

[19] James Froude: *History of England* (1867).

at the university, he jogged along the road between Nottingham and Cambridge.

If they travelled in a carter's wagon, it was almost certainly owned by the Hobson family of Cambridge who had established one of the first public transportation systems in England.[20] Generally students went in groups for better protection against highwaymen and vagabonds who infested the roads and preyed on a lone traveller.[21]

Chief Justice Coke has offered a post-Elizabethan appraisal of Cambridge: 'The suns, eyes, and minds of the kingdom from which religion, liberal education, and sound learning are spred most abundantly to every point of the realm.'[22] A modern historian equates Cambridge, 1500–1650, with 'nurseries of the Church' and credits the Protestant movement in Cambridge with nurturing the Reformation in England.[23]

Not only controversial theology but also advances in learning created the climate for William Lee, admitted at Christ's College, later at St. John's. Though it seems retrospectively that the tragic turn of events in the career of the inventor appears to stem from Lee not being in the right place at the right time, it can be argued that his terms at the university were at a unique time, when tutors, College Fellows, and university theologians took some considerable part in changing doctrines of religious thought. With movement toward liberalism an intellectual renaissance proved to be its counterpart.

This renaissance was affected not least by the efforts of Sir Walter Mildmay. In 1583, already renowned as Chancellor in the Queen's service, he had returned to the scene of his Alma Mater, Christ's College, buying the Priory of the Teaching Friars on Preacher's Street with the purpose that the old church of clerical times would become the 'seed

[20] Trevelyan: op. cit.
[21] L. F. Salzman: *English Trade in the Middle Ages* (1931).
[22] Craig R. Thompson: *Universities in Tudor England* (1959).
[23] H. C. Porter: *Aspects of Religious Life and Thought in the University of Cambridge, 1500–1650* (1958).

ground' of the new. As the founder of Emanuel College, he expressed 'the one object . . . to render as many possible fit for the administration of the Divine Word'. He chose for its Master, Lawrence Chaderton, to train '. . . Godly Pastors . . . a thing necessary above all others'.[24]

It was at Cambridge University, under the influence of Chaderton and his pupil William Perkins in their exposition of the new doctrines, that William Lee was to awaken to a changing world.

There was a goodly heritage in scholarship at Cambridge when he entered. Erasmus, as a leader in humanism, had left his mark lecturing there in an earlier period. Later, still identified with the University's progress, Erasmus commented: '. . . there existed literature, mathematics, a new Aristotle and Greek now'. In Lee's day there was the Erasmian edition of the New Testament. Also, in addition to Latin and Greek and modern languages, there were studies in Hebrew, Chaldee, Syriac, and Arabic under Lancelot Andrewes, first holder of the Greek scholarship, whose name is linked with an historic group identified as the Cambridge exponents of the new doctrines in practical divinity.[25]

On the other hand, retarded by the chains of the alchemists, the teaching of chemistry proceeded slowly. Studies in botany and zoology were advancing, freed increasingly from the tenets of mythology, and the door was slowly opening to medicine. Reflecting Elizabethan England's growing interest in distant waters and new lands, there was similar interest in courses in geography, astronomy, cartography, magnetism and navigation. Contributions in these areas of learning came from such pioneers as William Gilbert, of St. John's, who offered his knowledge of magnetism in the publishing of his De Magnete in 1600. Later, based on information contained therein, two actual instruments of navigation were constructed.

Also in Lee's time the work of Edward Wright was noteworthy, in the translation of the first study of logarithms

[24] Porter: op. cit.   [25] E. Isaacson: Life and Death of Andrewes (1650).

from Latin into English. Wright applied its mathematical data to navigation, finally leading to a voyage to the Azores.[26] For university admission Lee may not have found the entrance requirements democratic for there was discrimination within college walls. Roger Ascham, earlier at Christ's and St. John's, eminent in his service as the Queen's tutor, expressed his resentment like this: 'rich commoners or pensioners who come to the university without serious intellectual purpose, distract the more sober sort'.[27] Fellowcommoners, who dined with College Fellows as if nobles, had enviable privileges including the convenient one of getting degrees without completion of ordinary requirements.[28]

With tutors playing favourites, inequities were not lessened. As late as 1587 Lord Burghley, Chancellor of Cambridge, was informed, 'tutors favoured those who could pay them high stipends ... the richer be so corrupt with liberty and remissness that the tutor is afraid to displease his pupil through the desire of great gain'.[29]

How might William Lee, son of a diligent yeoman, with purpose to train in divinity, respond to that sector of college-mates who wore 'excessive ruffs, swords and rapiers ... broke academic rules, in pastimes such as cards, dice, fencing, bear-baiting'? At the tender but mature age of fifteen he may even have been more sobered by the unfairness of their privileged position ... 'and for *excuse*, when they ruffle and roist it out in riotous company ... think it sufficient to say they are *gentlemen*, which grieveth many not a little'.[30]

Due to the increasing interest in education on the part of Elizabeth and her Court, gentlemen and sons of nobility

[26] R. T. Gunther: *Early Science at Cambridge* (1937).
[27] 'Commoner' and 'pensioner', used interchangeably; defined as noble or wealthy youth, who was not a recipient of college funds.
[28] Thompson: op. cit.
[29] Trevelyan: op. cit.
[30] Rev. William Harrison: *Description of the Island of Great Britain* 2nd Edition (1587).

were receiving first place at the universities, lessening the openings for those of lower social status. Lee apparently was well-qualified, for his admission as a 'sizar' had met with no obstacles. In this classification he would be required to perform such lowly tasks for fellow-students, noblemen and pensioners, and personal service for Masters and Fellows.

For food, the sizar ate the 'leavings' from his betters' tables. It may be assumed that they were meagre, for dinner consisted of a 'penny piece of beef among four, having a few of the pottage made of the broth of the same beef, with malt and oatmeal'.[31] Perhaps, for the sizar, here was a blessing in disguise, even though seemingly he was deprived of a social refinement, introduced in 1575, a few years before Lee's matriculation:

> It is agreed the Master and the fellowes shall every one of them have ij table napkins boughte by the College . . . of (with) this condition that every fellowe at his departure shall deliver unto the Master ij whole table napkins for the use of his successoure . . . if either fellowe or pensionner do wipe his hande or finger off the table clothe he shall paye for every time ij to the use of the commons.

Among the 14 signatories to this document of privilege and penalty was Thomas Patenson, Lee's Tutor.[32]

Significantly, a prerequisite for acceptance as a sizar was a high intelligence to qualify for helping others with their studies.[33] The first steps in Lee's matriculation were to have his name entered in the Grace-Book Delta, in the Registry, pay his matriculation fee and receive the name of his Tutor.[34]

---

[31] Thompson: op. cit.
[32] John Peile: *Christ's College* (1900).   [33] Thompson: op. cit.
[34] *Grace-Book Delta*: University Archives, Old Schools Cambridge. The name of William Lee, surname spelled 'Leighe' (as usual in that period), is entered in the Grace-Book Delta, on page 306, May-Jul. 1579, 'W. Leighe', column 'Quadrantori'. On page 335, May 1579 it is also entered as 'W. Leighe'. Matriculation 'Sizar'. Tutor Mr. Patenson. No explanation is given for the double entry.

On appearing before the Master he would have taken an oath pledging to preserve the peace, obey the authorities, and defend the interests, of the university. Being the son of a yeoman, his matriculation fee was a nominal one, certainly less than the 40 shillings paid by William Cecil, later Lord Burghley, when as one of the gentry he matriculated as a pensioner in 1535.

Since most of the poorer students were destined for the Church, and the richer for the world, frugality took over from privilege. Many of the students slept four in a room, shared by the Tutor. Early rising at four in the morning was the rule, followed by common prayer from six to seven, with an 'exhortation of God's word' in the chapel where daily attendance was enforced. The morning was spent in private study or attending common lectures, and after the noon meal there was the period of study until the evening meal. Even mealtime had its ordered pattern, with conversation in Latin required and the Bible read aloud at dinner. After dinner 'they go further to reasoning in problems, or to some other study, until nine or ten o'clock, and then, being without fire and fain to walk or run up and down half an hour to get a heat on their feet, when they go to bed'.[35]

However, it should not be imagined that Lee's daily life was entirely drab and without excitement. Then, as now, students engaged in those extra-curricular activities forbidden or frowned upon by the authorities. Sometimes, it would appear that their Tutors were also men of action and flesh and blood. Such a one proved Thomas Patenson, listed as William Lee's Tutor. Patenson received his M.A. at Christ's in 1572 and was a Fellow there 1568–1581.[36] In 1576 his action as a Proctor was complained of by the town officials when it was charged that he, responsible for maintaining correct student behaviour, 'threatened to enter by force the home of John Goldsborowe, in the night-time'.

---

[35] Styrpe: *Ecclesiastical Memorials of the Reformation* (1721).
[36] John Peile: *Biographical Register (1505–1905) Christ's College* (1910).

When a Justice of the Peace, hearing of the matter, ordered Patenson 'to keep the peace', his defiant answer was 'to get himself home' . . . otherwise . . . 'he would sett him home'.

That night the tutor kept his threat when with his company (supposedly students on the side of honour) he accosted Goldsborowe, accusing him of misleading students from the path of morals prescribed by the university.[37] The Proctor's quarrel with the accused in front of the house of his father, Alderman Goldsborowe, attracted a crowd of the Alderman's supporters so that the dispute developed into 'Townsmen versus Gownsmen' with Patenson in the middle of the fray.

The Proctors or tutors considered it their responsibility to correct student deviations from rules by flogging. It is recorded that John Milton, the poet, who was at Christ's 1625–1632, gave his tutor cause for him to be thus disciplined.[38] Phillip Stubbes, author of *Anatomy of Abuses* (1583), was flogged for 'insolent and pragmatical conduct'. Ironically, as a writer of the social behaviour of the period, he is credited with 'moral treatises and indignant satires rebuking the age for its sins, real or fancied'.

That the standard of learning in Christ's was high may be noted when, ten years before Lee's time, Sir William Cecil, the Queen's Secretary of State, in his post as Chancellor of Cambridge arranged for the Queen's Progress to the University. Writing to the Master of Christ's he was anxious with 'desire that *order* (to mean both religion and civil behaviour) especially appeare in the universities', and also 'what manner of plesures in lerninge may be presented to her Majestie, who hath knowledge to understand very well in all common sciences'.

Christ's Master, Edward Hawford, revealed in his answer both the level of scholarship at the College and its regard for the attitude of the Court for learning, as generated by the scholarly Elizabeth. He offered 'to put themselves in all

---

[37] C. H. Cooper: *Annals of Cambridge* (1842).
[38] Louis B. Wright: *Middle Class Culture in Elizabethan England* (1935).

readiness to pleasure her with all manner of scholastical exercises, viz., with sermons, both in English and Latin; disputations in all kinds of all faculties; and playing of comedies and trajedies; and orations and verses both in Latin and Greek to be made and set up of all students'.[39]

The knowledgeable Elizabeth could not have been disappointed with the 'pleasures in lerninge' served her, though she may have been fatigued. Lord Burghley must have been both pleased and relieved, for government had an active role in academic affairs. Though the Vice-Chancellor, elected by the heads of the colleges, presided over the day-to-day business of the university, and the Proctors enforced university discipline, the control of university policy and decisions rested finally in the Chancellor's hands. In 1570 Chancellor Burghley had exercised his authority in the academic dismissal of Thomas Cartwright from the Chair of Divinity, for delivering lectures critical of the Established Church. Fortunately for Cambridge Burghley's was considered a measured and conservative direction in that period of religious history in the making.[40]

Chroniclers of the Queen's Progress have entered in the account the element of drama, intrinsic in the royal presence, not omitting the typical spectacular in dress: 'the Queen's gowne of Black velvet pinked . . . a caul upon her head, set with pearles and precious stones . . . a hat, spangled with gold, and a bush of feathers.' And too, her responsiveness to the gift presented by the Master at Christ's.[41] Perhaps years later, when Lee was working on his machine so painstakingly and hopefully to achieve stockings of silk for the Queen, sketched on the canvas of his memory was her reported delight with the pair of gloves she accepted from the Master, Edward Hawford, who was also Lee's Master when he was a student at Christ's.

As the stepping stone for the study of theology, the B.A. course required rhetoric in the first year, logic in the second

[39] Francis Peck: *Desiderata Curiosa* (1779).
[40] Porter: op. cit.   [41] Peck: op. cit.

and third, and philosophy in the fourth. The training in logic was preparatory to the student's participation in disputations held in the college and university halls. Given by professors in each faculty, the lectures supplied the undergraduate with topics he could use in disputations; the debates tested the student's knowledge and skill.

William Lee was one of 277 in his term who received a B.A. degree. He was examined by the Proctors and Regent Masters, and presented his *supplicat* to the Vice-Chancellor and Senate. Now a 'questionist', he was interrogated briefly at a ceremony and after 'responding' was ready to 'determine'.[42]

The procedure in taking the M.A. was similar to that described for the B.A. Considered as the 'most important single achievement in academic life was the Master's degree, with its right to teach or lecture anywhere, instruct undergraduates, preside at disputations, and share in the government of the university'.[43]

Calculating that the divinity course took seven years, following the seven years required to fulfil the B.A. and M.A. requirements, evidence based on the existing biographical data seems to suggest that Lee's training in theology was through the studies for the Arts and Masters degrees, which embraced training in religion, confirming the premise that 'in a Tudor University, theology was inescapable'.[44] Attendance by graduates and undergraduates was compulsory at the Latin sermon, the *Clerum*, addressed to resident Divines. All below the status of M.A. and excluding Fellows were obliged to attend every holy day eve to 'listen, and answer when questioned'. The interrogation was in the hands of the Catechist who was a strict leader. Penalties for non-attendance for a *puer* (under eighteen years of age) was a whipping; for an *adultus*, a fine of 2d.

On Sundays the entire university was required to attend both the morning and afternoon sermons preached by the University Regents. These were delivered in Great St.

[42] Peile: op. cit.   [43] Thompson: op. cit.   [44] Ibid.

Mary's, with the townspeople invited; tiers were erected on wooden scaffolding accommodating the M.A.s on moveable benches while the B.A.s stood or squatted on stools. Regularly at three in the afternoon on Saturdays and Sundays the Lancelot Andrewes lectures were held in the College Chapel, expounding the Ten Commandments. Andrewes, who was one of the moderates among the exponents of the new Puritan doctrines, was linked with another of this brotherhood, William Perkins, both setting new higher standards for the role of the preacher.[45]

William Perkins was Catechist of Christ's College and he 'made the hearers' hearts fall down and hairs to stand upright' as they listened to his preachings on the practical, the newly emphasized aspect of Christian life.[46] Years later, as significant as the historians' praise of this former student, tutor, and Fellow at Christ's, was that expressed by the 'sometimes students at Christ's'. Among the latter was Sam Ward who was seven years at Christ's and later Master at Sidney Sussex College. He records that Perkins 'by his doctrine and life did much good to the University . . . made it his holy day's exercise to resolve cases of conscience'. He thanked God 'that I came to this College in Perkins' time'.[47]

One can but speculate if William Lee, too, 'thanked God' for being contemporary 'in Perkins' time'. Evidence seems to suggest that he was certainly among those who sat at his feet during his impressionable years. Perkins was identified with Lee's own college, entering as a pensioner in 1578, becoming Christ's Catechist, and serving his Fellowship there until 1595. Moreover, as a sizar, Lee's duties included service to Fellows. Many students stayed with Perkins, who kept open house, and his interpretation of the moral law which was basic to practical divinity could but influence them profoundly.[48]

[45] Porter: op. cit.
[46] T. Fuller: *The History of the Worthies of England* (1840) edition.
[47] Porter: op. cit.   [48] Ibid.

Joining Perkins among the Puritan moderates at Cambridge in the 1580s was Perkins's tutor, Lawrence Chaderton. One later day, Lee might have gained encouragement from the perseverance and initiative shown by Chaderton. His Catholic father in protest at his son's turning to the new doctrines wrote to Chaderton, 'Here is a shilling, buy a wallet, go and beg'. Later he disinherited him.

Chaderton's progress was marked by steadfast conviction in his chosen doctrine. Eking out his scanty means by preaching, he attained a Fellowship at Christ's and was finally appointed by Sir Walter Mildmay, founder of Emanuel College, as its Master 'to train Godly Ministers'.[49]

Lee may have been impressed with this spiritual, intellectual brotherhood which included also Richard Greenham, who was to hold for twenty years a 'Godly pastorship'. They met together for scholarly exposition of the Scriptures, study of the Bible in the original languages, and discussion of the 'doctrines and true sense of the Bible'.

With his direction toward Theology, Lee's outlook inevitably will have been coloured by this academic warfare waged between Puritan and Anglican, with the moderates in the corner. Even on matters of casting support in the election of a College Head or Fellow, especially over questions of ceremonial, some partisanship was inescapable. Later, there was sharp controversy over Presbyterian versus Episcopal forms of church government.[50] Under Mary a number of scholars had been driven to exile and beheadings in the sixteenth century included five Chancellors of Cambridge. Non-conformity was called 'treason'.

If he were impressed with the Perkins group for its leadership in pursuit of 'pietie and learning' and its loyalty to the Crown and the University, none the less Lee must have perceived that individualism in the university was alien to the state-controlled church. Even in his time, Papists were excluded from university degrees. Their secret leanings were under strict surveillance as was apparent from the

[49] Ibid.   [50] Ibid.

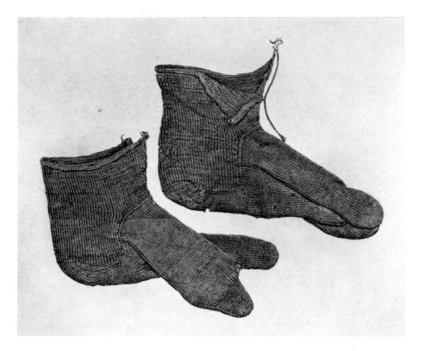

5. Hand-knitted wool socks found in an Egyptian tomb and ascribed to the fourth–fifth century B.C.

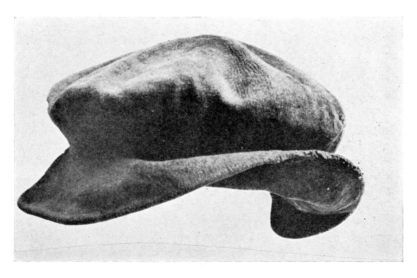

6. A cap of 'wolle knitte' as prescribed by the Cappers Act of 1571: 'Upon pain to forfeit for every day of not wearing, 3s. 4d.'

7. The Rev. William Lee (source unknown).

public burnings of books and vestments in the college court.[51] The high price of academic freedom reflected that of religious freedom in a university controlled by Church and State.

At Christ's, while he was in training for Holy Orders, he heard no doubt of the expulsion of John Mullen in 1573. Mullen's 'crime' had been that he deplored the status of the preacher in England: they . . . 'do not only not advance and set forward the edifying of the church. . . . 12 diligent men would do more good in England than all the preachers that now be'.[52] None the less, the storm of criticism increased as it centred on the system of the non-resident pluralists[53] in the ministers group 'who tarry in their college'; on the un-licensed preacher; on the sermon's content 'that does not edify more than a boy of 8 years will do'.[54] Lee was to find that the 'lerning and pietie' gap was to close but slowly.

A twentieth-century writer, in viewing this period in English religious history at Cambridge, shows how power-fully the university training influenced the development of the students. Under the college system of Fellows, the pupils, who could number from one to twenty, lived with the don, directly paid him, and were entirely controlled by him;[55] other sources of influence he suggests, the 'parental one' and 'the tradition of the native heath' were subsidiary. The nature of the Lee father-son relationship seems to suggest that the university also served William Lee *in loco parentis*.

At Cambridge the intellectual movement, coefficient of the religious one, included the influence of the leaders of the new religious doctrines whose survival extended to their written works, which to some degree were compilations of

---

[51] Thompson: op. cit.
[52] Peile: op. cit.
[53] 'Non-Resident Pluralist' the holding by one person of two or more benefices; 'Parson-Dons, Cambridge' also in the role of non-resident pluralist; 'Curate' was in actual charge of parish.
[54] Thompson: op. cit.
[55] Porter: op. cit.

their sermons. William Perkins was the first of the Cambridge 'best selling authors'. His publications, numbering forty, were popular for a generation after his death in 1602. The measure of value for the student was not only in the content of the writings but the skill manifested in the exposition.

Robert Hill, of St. John's, in publishing a translation of Perkins's *A Golden Chaine*, said of the tutor-preacher-author '. . . an excellent gifte he had, to define properly, divide exactly, dispute subtly, answer directly, speak pithily, write judiciously'.[56] If Lee were impressed with these skills of Perkins as implied by his publisher, viz. preciseness, selectivity, relevance, balance, and judgment . . . adding up to the 'virile and methodical intellect' of Perkins, there may have been indeed a formative situation for the prospective inventor. Perkins's aim to raise the quality and status of England's preachers is indicated in his specification regarding the preparation of the sermon, 'not to be written but spoken by heart . . . fit both for the people's understanding and to express the majestie of the Spirit'. In that period the homily was a ready-made sermon required to express religious attitudes acceptable to the government. Perkins's standard for the originally conceived 'not-to-be-written' sermon must have overwhelmed or enlightened more than one divinity student.

William Perkins found an attentive audience even when preaching in the general assembly at Cambridge's famous Stourbridge Fair, then considered the greatest of all English Fairs. He often directed his plainly worded, simple themes to the commercial classes. In his approach his note was one of encouragement, correlating the value and dignity of business with godliness. There was exhortation for two sets of values: 'as they may better their estates through buying and selling, they should help their souls by taking home some grain of the gospel'.[57]

The Stourbridge Fair—carnival, side-show, and mer-

---

[56] Porter: op. cit.   [57] Wright: op. cit.

chandise mart all in one—was situated on the stubble of the town-fields between the New Market and the river, occupying an area half a mile square. Held annually for a three-week period, it provided a highlight in the lives of Cambridge students, due in part to the university's association with it; the Vice-Chancellor in full academic pomp and splendour officially proclaimed its opening.[58]

For William Lee, imaginative and alerted to the novel and extraordinary, the Fair may have opened new horizons and stimulated curiosity in a wider world. Students and townspeople were greeted with cries of hawkers and apprentices:

> *What d'ye lack? What d'ye lack?*
> *Who'll buy my Sweet . . . sweet lavender?*
> *Sixteen branches for a penny . . .*
>
> *Pins! Three rows a penny!*
> *Pins! Buy of the Maker.*

Commodities gathered from the far-away lands found a place there in this great September market: silks, velvets, and glass from Italy and Venice, linens from Liege and Bruges, ironwork from Rouen. From Norway came tar and lumber; from Gascony, wines. There were furs and amber from the Hanse towns, dried and salted fish from the Baltic. Porcelains from the East were shown together with pierced copper and brasswork from Northern Algiers. From England's Cornwall tin was sold for future delivery, as well as leather from Northampton.

But of all the home produce that Lee may have been attracted to, the wool-packs from Leicestershire and his own Nottinghamshire took first place. Every year the freemen of Nottingham journeyed to the Fair with pack horses and wains, wool-laden, returning with stocks of cured fish from the Baltic traders. In the 'Duddery', where woollen goods were sold, perhaps he gained his first knowledge of foreign

[58] Salzman: op. cit.

trade; it was reported that in one week £100,000 worth of merchandise changed hands, additional to the quantity ordered by traders for future delivery, estimated to be £50,000.

So at Cambridge Lee found a call in the two directions: to things spiritual and to things temporal. This indeed was William Perkins's call. The emphasis on the practice of thrift, diligence, and work was in terms of man's opportunity to serve God, complemented by his capacity to labour for the good of the community. The popular writings of Perkins conveyed this theme even to the colonists of far-off America in its throes of commercial enterprise: 'God bestowes his giftes upon us . . . that it be profitable to his glorie and commonweal'. The teachers of the Reformation learnt from Perkins and his disciples the earlier lesson of Luther, to dignify the gospel of work as founded on Scripture, thus negating mendicancy, the product of idleness, and its associations with Romish practices.[59] For the middle-class, with the conception of the value of human labour related to the godliness of responsible endeavour, the cornerstone of the pursuit of trade was laid within the structure of the Protestant ethic.

Juxtaposed to the pursuit of trade is the pursuit of wealth, for which Perkins set the criteria: honesty in trading and, in utilization of worldly goods, moderation as befits the status and conditions of the[60] individual. Basic in his teachings and writings is the theory of individual differences: 'Every man must choose a fit calling to walk in; that is every callinge must be fitted to the man, and every man to be fitting to his callinge . . .; a personal callinge . . . arising of that distinction which God makes between man and man in every societie.'[61] One future day how would Lee, a curate-inventor, resolve the choice?

Histories of Cambridge record that Perkins's reputation

59 Wright: op. cit.
60 Ibid. Referring to Perkins's, 'Second and Third Bookes of Conscience'.
61 William Perkins: Workes (numerous printings and editions).

as a teacher was unrivalled. Few students left the university without having sought him in 'cases of conscience'. In Christ's dining-hall among the portraits of twenty-one Cambridge worthies and benefactors (chosen as 'glass-worthy' and placed in 1852 in the lights of the west-oriol window), and in the company of Charles Darwin, Sir Walter Mildmay, John Milton, and others, are set the images of William Perkins and of William Lee.[62]

Cambridge University memorialized both William Lee and William Perkins. The creativity of each has survived.

[62] Indebted for this information to Mrs. A. Beatty, Sub-Librarian, Christ's College.

THREE

Conflict in the Glebe House

HAVING matriculated at Christ's in 1579, William Lee subsequently removed to St. John's, being a member of that college from 1580. There he proceeded to take his B.A. degree in 1582–83, where 'it is believed he received his M.A. degree in 1586'.[1]

The granting of an M.A. degree by St. John's would have entitled William Lee to ordination. Being twenty-three years old, he would have met the requirement of age and also, 'none shall be made Minister, unless it appears to the Bishop that he is of honest life, professes the doctrines expressed in the 39 Articles of Faith, and is able to answer and render an account of his faith in Latin . . . or have special ability or gifts to be a preacher'.[2]

The adoption many years later by the Frame-Work Knitters Guild of a coat of arms showing a figure in the dress of a clergyman on one side of a stocking-frame and a woman on the other, the woman holding a pair of knitting needles in one of her hands and a spindle in the other, is evidence that the Guild held the belief that Lee was ordained a clergyman.

He had to make the compulsory declaration of the Oath of

---

[1] In the nineteenth century, in his *Biographical Register of Christ's College*, John Peile wrote: 'Lee is said to have M.A., of which I have no trace.' In substantiation of Lee having received an M.A., as opposed to the ambiguity of the records at St. John's, we have the statements of the three seventeenth-century writers. In 1630 Stow wrote, 'Mr. Lee, M.A. of St. John's College devised the knitting of silk stockings'; in 1677, Thoroton wrote, 'At Calverton was born William Lee, Master of Arts in Cambridge'; in 1689 Dr. Howell, in his *History of the World*, ascribed the invention to the 'Rev. William Lee, Master of Arts in Cambridge'.

[2] Henry Cripps: *Laws of the Church and Clergy* (1863).

Supremacy, which authorized church affairs under the Crown:

The Queen's Highness is the only Supreme Governor of this realm . . . in all spiritual and ecclesiastical things or causes. That no foreign Prelate has any jurisdiction, ecclesiastical or spiritual . . . therefore I shall bear the true faith and allegiance to his heirs and lawful successors.[3]

In meeting the requirements for ordination concerning 'the special gifts or ability to be a preacher', Lee may have hoped to emulate the high standard set by William Perkins or, conscious of the storm of criticism at Cambridge on the prevailing low standard of preaching in England, perhaps he developed some anxiety! University trained, he would be eligible under the church statute to preach: 'no person shall be admitted to any ecclesiastical living, or suffered to preach, except that he be licensed . . . by the Archbishop or by the Bishop . . . or by one of the two universities'. The availability of St. Wilfrid's Church in Calverton fulfilled his 'tithe to orders', that 'he should have some certain place where he may use his function'. Ordination would have been in the diocese, most probably in St. Mary's Church in Nottingham, though there is no record of this.

As a curate, Lee would be in active charge of the Calverton parish. His stipend would have been £4 10s. yearly; the yearly income of a non-resident benefice might be £200. If he glanced back to the church he knew before his terms at Cambridge, he might remember the parish parson as a sometime small farmer, cultivating the acres of glebe-land belonging to the church.[4]

In pre-Elizabethan times a parson might agree with a weaver to pay him a quarter of corn for three-quarters of a yard of scarlet cloth.[5] Even as late as 1640 Church livings in Nottinghamshire were £30 a year while the benefice of the non-resident pluralist rated £175.[6]

---

[3] 2. Elizabeth: C1. & C2.
[5] Thomason Tracts.
[4] S. T. Bindoff: *Tudor England* (1950).
[6] Ibid.

When Lee was at Cambridge, a subject of heated discussion was the inequities of the Anglican Church hierarchy; protests were made against the Episcopal system and pluralists,[7] with its yield of underpaid parish parsons.[8] In the Parliament of 1563 the bill to provide more adequate income for vicars and curates received short shrift, possibly because taxation on the householder was involved.[9] A similar bill met the same fate in the 1581 Parliament, just a few years before Lee was reading the Elizabethan Prayer-Book in St. Wilfrid's.[10] During Lee's time Parliament did not legislate to raise the income of the parish incumbent, nor did the respect and regard of the parish for its Shepherd show much improvement.

That clerical poverty tended to prolong pluralities and the attendant evils was evident in Calverton before and after Lee. In 1559 neglect was the price of the neglected parson, for there appeared in a church visitation report 'the chancel of the church at Calverton . . . nearly fallen down'. In 1656, in the Commissioner's report on qualifications of all candidates for church livings, 'at Calverton, James Stevenson was removed, and being destitute, aged and impotent had to be given relief by the justices'.[11]

The pattern of Lee's life at Calverton can be gleaned from descriptions of a model parish in the charge of another member of Perkins's group whom Lee probably met at Cambridge. He was Richard Greenham, known as a 'godly pastor', who held the parish for twenty years at Dry Drayton, five miles from Cambridge. Rising at 4 a.m., preaching twice on Sundays, catechizing the children, reading thrice daily from the Scriptures to family and friends, the pastor found

---

[7] 'Non-Resident Pluralist'. See note 53 on p. 33 *supra*.

[8] Bindoff: op. cit. The Episcopal system was charged with a mercenary system of Bishops; replacement was sought of Presbyterian system with equity in Doctors, Deacons, Elders, Pastors.

[9] J. E. Neale: *Elizabeth I and her Parliaments* (1953).

[10] 5 Eliz. C. 5.

[11] Alfred C. Wood: *Nottinghamshire in the Civil Wars* (1937).

time and interest for the surrounding farmers as counsellor and friend. Greenham's writings disclose that though great importance was attributed to knowledgeable preaching, the individual approach was basic, 'to deal wisely with an affected conscience, and discreetly and soundly with an heretic'.[12]

The ecclesiastical climate of a small parish is indicated by the canonical legislation passed by the Convocation.[13] The curate's place of influence was hedged in between the Bishop's and that of the churchwarden. It was to the Bishop that the parson would need to report annually 'names of all parishoners over 14, who did not go to Holy Communion'; church attendance was compulsory with absentees subject to fine. The parson was 'to take heed, that young men, especially countrymen (whose nature is more prone to the contempt of godliness and disorder) neither ring bells, neither walk in the churches, nor have idle talk together, nor by laughing or noise or unhonest jesting, either hinder the Minister or offend the people'.

There was more than the problem of disorder in the church service. The churchwarden was to curb the over-zealous pedlar, 'which carries about and sells pins . . . and other small trifles', from offering his wares in the church-yards on Sundays or Holidays, and an eye needed to be kept on those tavern keepers inclined to Sunday business-as-usual '. . . to not allow anyone in their taverns during hours of divine service'.

That the secular arm tried to enforce church attendance was attested in the items in the Borough Records of Notting-ham, in 1587: 'Mistress Shereton, that she come not to church, fine xij d, and we presente John Shereton, that he come not to church xij d.'

Failure in family-worship and fines in another presentment are similarly recorded in 1589: 'We do presente James

---

[12] H. C. Porter: *Aspects of Religious Life and Thought in the University of Cambridge* (1958).
[13] Convocation of 1571: Canon Legislation.

Halloye xij d, for not coming to churche, and his two daughters, Ane xij d, and Frances xij d.'[14]

Lee may have been conscious that some attended church simply to avoid the penalty of fine. There is the story of the Catholic gentleman in Cornwall who endured the reading of the lesson and the congregational psalm singing of the 'Geneva Jig' but left church before the sermon, calling audibly to the parson in the pulpit, 'when thou art finished what thou has to say, come and dine with me'.[15]

Lee's pastoral duties would be based on the 39 Articles of Faith in the Anglican Church Creed and on the use of the Elizabethan Prayer Book. The official sermon was the Homily, considered by some in the pulpit a great opportunity to pontificate; for the parishioner, it may have furnished distraction as entertainment, or for some the message of Christianity. One can but conjecture that Lee would be inclined to follow the course of Perkins and Greenham, that 'the sermon not be written, but spoken by heart'. He may have favoured the expounding of Scriptures, as learned from the Cambridge reformers, but he will have been aware that some parishioners scoffed at this trend as the 'Scripture pedantry of the Puritan'.

In Lee's time at St. Wilfrid's Church the official Book of Homilies was decreed by the Queen and addressed to the Minister . . . 'to read and declare to their parishioners plainly and distinctly one of the said Homilies'. The two Bookes of Sermons or Homilies contained:

Certayne Sermons appoynted by the Queenes Majestie, to be declared and read, by all Parsons, Vicars and Curates every Sunday and Holyday in their churches; and by Her Graces advise, perused and overseene, for the better understanding of the simple people.[16]

[14] Borough Records of Nottingham.
[15] G. M. Trevelyan: *English Social History* (1944).
[16] L. B. Wright: *Middle Class Culture in Elizabethan England* (1935).

The Queen, aided and abetted by Lord Burghley her vigilant adviser, did indeed believe in the ready-made preachment and the principle that the pulpit should express views favourable to the Crown. The conclusion of the royal decree, 'when the foresaid Booke of Homilies is read over, her Majestie's plesure is, that the same be repeated and read againe, in such sort as was before prescribed' could have left but little doubt in the Calverton Preacher's mind as to the Queen's choice.[17]

William Lee may have accepted the notion that the Homily was designed to express values that the Queen wanted her people to identify with, 'when not many have the gifte of preaching sufficiently to instructe the people . . . ignorance will be maintayned, if some remedy be not speedily founde'. The remedy she urged may well have been the 'speedily founde one'.[18] In an age when she was aiming to build a *via media* to religion, she was assuming also that there was a royal road to preaching.

Queen Elizabeth considered that the Homily was also of value in promoting the security of the realm. For example, the final preachment in the Second Tome, written after the Rebellion of the North, contains a powerful message in condemnation of disobedience and its corollary of wilful rebellion. This addition to the second book derived from the Queen's fears that the climate of the times, domestic and foreign, conditioned by conflicts in religion and politics, was not yet free from the spirit of revolution.

In these two books of official exhortations the themes also stressed, in addition to homilies serviceable to the state, the prudential virtues and the negative effect of unthrifty vices.[19] Lee may have agreed with the Queen's designation of the scope of the Homily, 'better understanding of the simple people'. In villages like Calverton in this period, though the sons of the gentry began attending school, the mass of the small population was quite illiterate, or half-taught. For

[17] L. B. Wright: op. cit.   [18] Ibid.   [19] Ibid.

the laity as well as for some of the clergy, learning had not yet caught up with piety.[20]

In these standardized teachings, subjects of interest to apprentices and tradesmen were also treated. Perhaps the Cambridge-ordained pastor was puzzled by the official statement against 'fine clothes'. His conclusion may have been that a ready-made sermon failed to interpret the distinction between the 'lust for finery', with its attributed evil of taking money out of the country, and the acquisition of goods related to the pursuit of trade with its benefits for the commonweal—a lesson he learned at Cambridge in the new doctrines of practical divinity.[21]

Historians, in default of biographical data, have found it difficult to paint a picture of Curate William Lee exercising his calling in St. Wilfrid's. History does, however, offer a large canvas of the times from 1586, dating his return from St. John's College to the period of his invention of the knitting loom in 1589. His inner conflicts may have matched in intensity the instability of the nature of the times he lived in.

Two dramatic facts certainly emerge from this period of 'the lost years'. First, there was a growing alienation from his yeoman father, leading ultimately to the disinheritance by his son just as Lawrence Chaderton, Lee's tutor at Cambridge, was disinherited.

Secondly, and fundamental to this conflict between father and son, was William Lee's fateful decision to abandon his Curacy in favour of pursuing his invention.

To understand the conflict between the old era and new as expressed by such sharp disruption of family relationships, it is necessary to examine a little further the state of mind of William Lee and his yeoman father, both so typical of the times and of their own class in society.

William Lee, father of the Cambridge-trained curate, lived in a period caught in the overlap of the medieval, and the new and changing. The anti-clerical revolution brought

[20] Trevelyan: op. cit.   [21] Wright: op. cit.

reformed doctrines to Nottinghamshire, which sometimes seemed false and sometimes acceptable to him and his yeoman neighbours. A thrifty parishioner, his regular church attendance may have been conditioned simply by the non-attendance fine, as was indicated earlier; if for other motivation, and typical of some of his social class, 'as he sat in church, in his best clothes, though of simple dress, he was capable of only two prayers . . . for rain, and for fair weather . . . apprehending God's blessings only in a good year or a fat pasture'.[22]

If the religious meditations of the father did reflect a cow-and-plough ideology, it was born out of his constant, diligent exploitation of the resources of his land. With an earlier cutting down of Sherwood Forest he had taken care of his family's and the market's needs by developing 'open field' farming. The enterprising freeholder, cultivating his own land, added sheep to his corn for wool production in the Midlands in Elizabeth's reign. To meet increased wool production, arable land was converted to pasturage by enclosure of the common. For the Lees this change in practice netted larger sheep pastures and the reaping of the higher prices out of the fruit of the loom. For some of their neighbours, whose tenure was insecure, it meant deprivation of their piece in the commons.

This practice in itself may have produced a conflict between father and son. History records that the enclosure system brought injustices, finally depopulating villages and increasing vagabondage. In that period the pursuit and progress of industries in the country districts was accompanied by periodic unemployment. Because the care of the enemployed, under the Poor Laws, was the responsibility of the parish, curate William Lee could have been gravely concerned at the problem as he sat in the Glebe House.[23]

Land was the be-all and end-all of the yeoman's way of thinking. In the provisions of his father's will the feature of

[22] Albert J. Schmidt: *The Yeoman in Tudor and Stuart England* (1961).
[23] Trevelyan: op. cit.

land receives reference of the greatest importance. In that century, 'not only did the yeoman buy land . . . he laboured endlessly for greater profits from his land, in order that he could purchase more land'.[24] However, there was another kind of value, more relative than absolute, that his son heard at Cambridge from William Perkins . . . 'Occupation (ed: trade and industry) is as good as land, because land may be lost, but skill and labour in good occupation is profitable to the end, because it will helpe at a neede when lande and all things faile.'[25] Here was another point of conflict between father's and son's ways of thinking.

The gentry had a wider glimpse of life than the surrounding yeoman. They had better schooling, social prestige, and took part in local politics. They apprenticed their younger sons to trade and were not ashamed to acknowledge a son in trade in an age of growing commercial activity.[26] Unlike the social class above him, William Lee the Elder as family head was inclined to conserve his country roots; the yeoman was averse to change, 'for wealth comparable with the gentle sort (gentry) will not for all that, change his condition, nor desire to be apparelled with the titles of gentry'.[27]

Because the yeoman rejected fashions other than his traditional russet ones, another source of alienation from his son perhaps may have been the latter's identification with the university student fashions: 'they did go disorderly in Cambridge, wearing . . . scabilonions and knit nether stocks, too fine for scholars'.[28] As he came to hear of it he may have worried that the very purpose of his son's invention was to create still another item for finer dress. The paternal resentment against this fashion-changing might match the attitude expressed by another yeoman father to his son:

The time has been when as a Norfolk yeoman
Would wear such cloth as this sheep's russet gray
And, for my son shall be no precedent

[24] Schmidt: op. cit.   [25] W. Perkins: *Werkes*.   [26] Trevelyan: op. cit.
[27] E. M. Lambarde: *Perambulations of Kent* (1576).   [28] Porter: op. cit.

To break those orders, come, off with this trash . . .
Let trueborn gentlemen wear gentry's robes
and yeomen, country-seeming liveries.[29]

Living in rural isolation, an industrious yeoman like William Lee's father rarely journeyed. He was not in direct touch with London nor did he hear news of university life. In Nottingham, such news as reached him may have caused him to consider Cambridge suspect of 'heresy'. A scandal of the times concerned the son of Nottingham's Mayor Robert Alvey, Henry, who attended Christ's and later was a Fellow at St. John's where he was reported to have participated in the presbytery movement. As a strict parent, Lee the Elder may have been more disturbed by news of the changes implicit in the new doctrines and reforms at his son's university, and less aware of the movement by its teachers and preachers to interpret the pertinence of theology to the pursuit of life.

The whole age, both spiritual and temporal, at the time in which father and son lived was in upheaval. William Lee's own inner religious conflicts will have added persuasion to the idea of abandoning his curacy. On his homecoming in Calverton, his family and neighbours in Nottinghamshire were already disturbed by the religious differences among the gentry of the old religion, raising fears of a Roman Catholic rebellion, following the arrival from the Continent shortly after 1580 of a Jesuit mission to England.[30] Curate William Lee had heard tell how his grandfather's father-in-law's pastorship suffered under the Marian Persecutions at the hands of the Catholics (1555–58). Now, in Lee's own time 'the Jesuits flitted about in disguise' hiding in priest holes, preparing a fifth column against the Protestants in England. The penalty on discovery was execution; though the crime was considered by the Elizabethan state as treason, not heresy as under Mary Tudor's reign, the penalty none

[29] Schmidt: op. cit. Quoted from *The Blind Beggar of Bednal Green* (1569).
[30] Bindoff: op. cit.

the less was just as severe.[31] This infiltration of Catholic missionaries worsened the climate of fear and suspicion, marked by the impending news of the Spanish invasion and the threat of the assassination of the Queen.

Thus during the years that Curate William Lee was at the Parsonage, the Glebe House in Calverton, the clash of the Anglican, Non-Conformist, and Catholic doctrines created a ground-swell of attitudes of intolerance, unfavourable for him in the exercise of his first calling as curate at St. Wilfrid's Church. There is some question whether, conscious of the inequities of the Elizabethan Church, he was sobered by or active with the Puritan groups made up of parish priests and Justices of the Peace in Nottinghamshire, working from within to overturn the Episcopal form in the Anglican Establishment. Though the Puritan moderates at Cambridge in Lee's time were loyal to the Crown, there is the fact that Perkins participated with the Alvey[32] group of university dons connected with the presbytery movement there.[33] Strong in their denunciation of the Episcopal system of Bishops, throughout the counties in Lee's time, they met in secret presbyteries; they amended the Elizabethan Prayer Book; and they expounded the Scriptures in ways which sought to undermine the structural pattern of the Anglican Church.[34]

The tension of the period further increased as a result of the Martin Marprelate tracts, secretly and anonymously printed inveighing against the Episcopal system of the Established Church. In 1584 the first pamphlet of a series was published in vehement protest against the Bishops. The attack was so abusive that it startled even some Puritans who feared it would hurt their cause. The counter-attacks by the government persisted a decade; in 1593 the official answer was by enactment of penalties, 'exile or death to any

---

[31] J. E. Neale: *Essays in Elizabethan History* (1963).
[32] Henry Alvey, Fellow St. John's 1577–87, Son of Mayor Alvey of Nottingham.
[33] Porter: op. cit.   [34] Bindoff: op. cit.

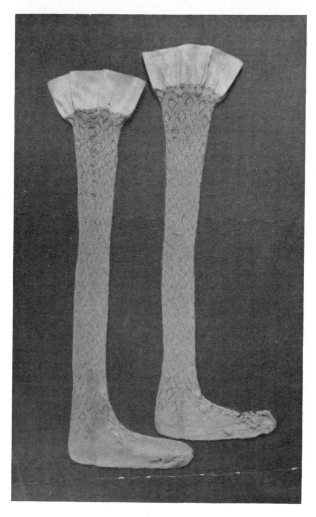

8. Queen Elizabeth's silk stockings, on view at Hatfield House, Hertfordshire.

Henry Carey
Lord Hunsdon

ÆTATIS SVÆ 66
AN. 1591.

9. Henry Carey, First Baron Hunsdon, who was Lee's patron at the court of Queen Elizabeth. Artist unknown.

and all who refused to attend church, or who attended unlawful meetings under pretense of any exercise of religion'.[35]

Such were some of the conflicts that must have caused Lee to lose heart in his sense of mission as curate. Again, on this score too he will have been in conflict with his father. The phraseology of the will of William Lee the Elder identifies him as a member of the Anglican Church; in bequeathing his 'soul to Christ' there is the omission of the reference to the 'Saints' included in the traditional testamentary form of the earlier clerical period.[36] That all was not quiet on the Nottinghamshire religious front was evidenced in 1603, when presentations showed, 'the Catholics were well-sprinkled throughout the county, little congregations of earnest yeomen assembled furtively for worship in its villages'.[37] There may have been more truth than humour that for some yeomen, 'religion was a part of the copyhold'.[38]

The regional historian can offer a final scene that relates to the basic alienating difficulties in the elder Lee's relations with his son: 'It may well be imagined that as William Lee's father drove his wain, on a Saturday morning to the Marketplace in Nottingham, and took his stand opposite St. Mary's Church, paying the stallage of 1d., before he unloaded his dairy products, he could not help but overhear words that may have been muttered against his son. He may have heard complaints and hints that his son was neglecting his sacerdotal duties, or heard slighting remarks about the "Vicar spending his time making a machine", and "that it would be better if he did God's work and not the work of Satan", and "that the loom would take the bread out of the mouths of honest craftsmen".'

It was not until the seventeenth century that the busy yeoman gave pause to consider that the concepts of thrift and industry emphasized in the Puritan creed were not out

[35] Craig R. Thompson: *The English Church in the 16th Century* (1958).
[36] A. J. Dickens: *The English Reformation* (1965).
[37] Alfred C. Wood: *Nottinghamshire in the Civil Wars* (1937).
[38] Schmidt: op. cit.

of harmony with his own yeoman pattern of living and its tenets.[39] In this earlier day, when William Lee left the Calverton Glebe House and abandoned the curacy, there was not yet in the parental attitude any acceptance of the change in his son's calling.

If the prospective inventor had detected any note in his father's farewell, it might have been that of the yeoman: 'I was a yeoman born, so I'll die; Then if you beest my son, be of my mind'.[40]

[39] Mildred Campbell: *The English Yeoman under Elizabeth and the Early Stuarts* (1942).
[40] Schmidt: op. cit.

FOUR

'Arte and Mysterie of Hand-Knitting'

THE prospective inventor's interest in the 'trueborn gentry-like' finer things such as silk-knit stockings may have stemmed from knowledge of his mother's and sisters' possessions and tastes. In the napery listed in the inventory of the will of William Lee, the Elder, the items '. . . pillows, napkins, tablecloaths, towels' were evidences of a higher level in their social class. In kitchen equipment, the more exceptional items were vessels of pewter, a step ahead in refinement from the wooden and earthenware in more common use. Denoting this higher standard were also the pewter candlesticks.

Being naturally of an inquiring turn of mind, when he first thought of inventing a loom to knit, Lee must have wondered about the origins of the 'mysterie' of weaving and knitting.[1]

From his studies in the Bible he would have known that the Egyptians, the Hebrews, and the peoples of the Bible lands were 'adept and skilful to execute all manner of work . . . of the designing weaver, of the embroiderer in blue and scarlet yarn . . . and in linen thread'.[2] His studies at Cambridge will have made him familiar with the passages in Homer describing how the Greeks were expert in weaving and spinning, the knowledge coming directly from the Gods: 'All the production of women's arts, as of spinning and weaving, are characterised as the work of Athena.'[3]

[1] Craft Guilds developed in 'Misteries'. The word is a variant of 'Mastery'.
[2] Exodus XXXV.
[3] *The Iliad* of Homer. Arthur Cullen Bryant's translation.

51

Aeons of time had elapsed from the day when a primitive prototype of Lee evolved the idea of weaving yarn on a loom. It is known that Neolithic man spun animal and vegetable fibres into yarns, and wove them into fabrics many thousands of years ago.[4] At some stage during the time continuum the idea of knitting yarn by hand was born, without benefit of a loom—the art of 'elastic-loop hand-knitting'.

Search as he might Lee would not have found one single written reference in the Old or New Testament to the art of hand-knitting. If he had travelled in the Near East near the Sea of Galilee, he might have heard an oral tradition that the fishermen, who followed the Apostle Peter, were accustomed to wear hand-knit caps on the waters.

It was only in 1945, 350 years after Lee made the first pair of stockings on his knitting loom, that archaeologists discovered remnants of knit-fabric dating back to A.D. 250. They were found in the ruins of the destroyed city of Dura Europos, near the borders of ancient Palestine.[5] [6]

Knowledge of the art of hand-knitting passed into Egypt and a general date of 4th–6th century A.D. has been established as the period when hand-knitted anklets, knit by members of the Coptic sect of Early Christians, were buried with the dead.[7] Relics of these anklets have survived until today.[8]

According to Marco Polo, the Venetian traveller of the thirteenth century who visited the Monastery of Barsamo,

[4] John Myers: *Primitive Man in Geologic Times* (Cambridge Ancient History 1923 Edition).

[5] *The Excavations at Dura Europos*. Yale University and the French Academy of Inscriptions and Letters (1945).

[6] Milton N. Grass: *History of Hosiery* (1955).

[7] Sir William M. F. Petrie: *Hawara, Biahmu and Srinoe* (1889).

[8] Victoria and Albert Museum, London Ref. Nos. 593–594. Kendrick: *Catalogue of Textiles from Burying Grounds in Egypt*. One pair of hand-knitted wool anklets is peculiarly noteworthy. Divided at the great toe, indicating it was worn with sandals, with the latchet of the sandal passing between the large and second toe, the element of fit was obtained by dropping stitches and cross-knitting at the heel, in a manner not dissimilar to the fashioning obtained in full-fashioned stockings.

near Tabriz in Persia in 1272, hand-knit woollen girdles were made there and were said to possess magical powers and 'were excellent things to remove bodily pain'. The story is that the monks were continuously knitting woollen girdles which they placed on the Altar of St. Barsamo during the services, the girdles thus acquiring marvellous powers. When the members of the Brotherhood went begging for alms, they presented these girdles to peasants and landowners, stressing their magic powers.[9]

The introduction of the art of hand-knitting into Europe was a result of war and conquest. In A.D. 641 the Arabs, under the Caliph of Mecca, conquered Egypt and found there a flourishing textile industry. The native Mohammedans and Christian Copts continued their weaving and knitting under the new masters. Spreading out in search for glory and new lands, in A.D. 711 the Arabs gained control of the Iberian Peninsula, bringing to the natives of Spain the Islamic arts and culture.

There are two hypotheses how the art of hand-knitting was then introduced in Spain. One is that the families of the troops, who followed the conquerors, practised the art and taught it to the natives. The other supposes that the early Coptic missionaries, who were sent to Spain and then to Italy, taught the art to the natives. With this knowledge and the development in the eleventh century A.D. of a flourishing sericulture, Spain became the cradle of the silk hand-knit stocking. It was not until the seventeenth century, when Fashion and Progress entered upon the scene clad in silk loom-knit stockings, that the Spanish Court impeded its step. An English courtier, in presenting a pair to the Spanish Ambassador for his Queen, received the frigid admonition: 'Take back thy stockings. And know, foolish sir, that the Queen of Spain hath no legs.'[10]

Hand-knitting was extensively practised in Italy as early as the thirteenth century. The hands of Pope Innocent IV,

[9] *The Voyages of Marco Polo:* Yule Edition.
[10] Grass: op. cit.

who died in 1254, were clothed in knit-silk gloves.[11] It was from Mantua, in Italy, that the legendary pair of hand-knit worsted stockings were brought to England, which William Rider in 1564 borrowed from the Italian merchant and 'caused other stockings to be made by them'.

In the early fourteenth century the widow of Duke Borislaus had knowledge of hand-knitting. She was the daughter of the Margrave of Pomerania and is described as having been 'a very prudent and moderate lady'. In her old age, when her sight became bad so that she was incapable of seeing or embroidering, she 'never put the needles out of her hand'.[12]

In France, not quite 100 years before Lee was to introduce his stocking-knitting loom, the Guild of the Hand-knitters of stockings (*La Communauté des Maîtres Bonnetiers au Tricot*) received their charger or 'Letter of Foundation' on August 16, 1527.[13] The yarns used by them in their hand-knitting were mainly linen or worsted. Silk did not come into common use until after the middle of the sixteenth century. It is a matter of note that Henry II, who came to the throne of France in 1547, wore hand-knitted silk stockings when he married Catherine de Medici in 1533; he also wore them on his death-bed when the marriage of his sister Margaret to the Duke of Savoy was solemnized in 1559.[14]

It was not until after 1560 in France, under Charles IX and Henry III, that the courtiers began to wear knit-silk stockings. After that, and in the period of the religious conflicts, 'the very citizens began to wear them, frequently'. The historian Mezeray wrote: 'It is an infallible observation that pride and luxury are most prominent during a public calamity.' After Henry IV came to the throne, in the early 1600s he developed his great interest in sericulture, which

---

[11] Hermstadt: *Grundiss der Technologie:* quoted by Chamberlain in *Knitted Footwear* (1950).
[12] Johan Beckmann: *History of Inventions* (1789).
[13] J. Savary des Bruslons: *Dictionnaire Universel du Commerce* (1723).
[14] François de Mezeray (1680): quoted in Nichols' *Progresses*.

led to the development of the French frame-work knitting industry in which Lee played such a great part as will be described later.[15]

Might not Lee have had a fleeting thought about his early brethren of the cloth, and their connection with hand-knitting? The sailor disciples of the 'Big Fisherman', the Apostle Peter, who were said to have made their own heavy wool-knit caps; the early Coptic-Christian missionaries, travelling to Spain and Italy to spread the Gospel, bringing their teaching of the art to those countries; St. Fiacre, the Irish Missionary, coming to France and becoming the Patron Saint of the French Guild of Hand-Knitters; the Monks of St. Barsamo who knit girdles said to possess 'magic curative powers' . . . these links of the church to the handicraft might have caused him to wonder.

In England, cut and sewn stockings, usually ill-fitting, were worn both by men and women at least 500 years before Lee and the introduction of hand-knit stockings. They were cut from whole pieces of coloured woven woollen or linen cloths by a member of the Merchant Taylors' Guild, measured and fitted to the leg and foot, and then seamed up the back. In 1087 when William Rufus, the second son of William the Conqueror, became King of England, he wore cut and sewn hose, 'a hose of say' and they 'cost a mark.[16] Cut and sewn hose had their counterpart in the French *Chausse*, the German *Heuses*, and the Italian *Cala*.

Stow relates that Henry VIII, always much concerned with the splendour of his raiment '. . . did only wear cloth hose, or hose cut out of ell-wide taffety'.[17] The cloth hose may have been for everyday wear while 'taffety', being a fine, smooth, glossy silk-fabric, was worn only on ceremonial and state occasions.

In its original sense the philological origin of the word

[15] de Mezeray: op. cit.
[16] Say = a twilled, worsted cloth.
[17] An 'ell' was a standard measurement for cloth, being about 45 inches in length.

'knit' antedates by many centuries the practice of the art of knitting by the Egyptians and the Syrians. It goes back to the Sanskrit word *Nahyat*, which had a connotation of '*net*' and also 'weave'.[18] Lee would have found that the word 'knit' had been used in the Anglo-Saxon and Old English words of 'cynttan', 'knitten', 'netten', 'chitten' and 'knotten', introduced into England by the invaders of the fifth and sixth centuries A.D. and having the connotation of 'binding together', 'uniting firmly', 'interlocking'.[19]

The earliest reference found to hand-knitting in England is in the middle of the fifteenth century. In Ripon, Yorkshire, in the records and accounts of a church for the years 1452–56 there is a will in which is listed, among other articles of wearing apparel, not a reference to 'knit stockings' but to 'one knyt gyrdll'.[20]

By the year 1488 knitting was associated with the concept of wearing apparel, long and importantly enough to be referred to in a sumptuary law. In the reign of Henry VII, an act was passed: 'The price of felted hats was to be 1s. 8d., while the price of "knytted" woollen caps should be 2s.'.[21] Even at this early period the intent of the sumptuary law was to sustain the employment of the hand-knitter by setting a higher price for knit caps over felt hats.

In 1552, during the reign of Edward VI, Parliament specified that 'knitte hose, knitte petticoates, knitte gloves and knitte slieves' were permitted to be purchased during the time allowed 'for buying and selling wooles'.[22]

---

[18] *Oxford English Dictionary*.

[19] Specimens of a fabric, made by a process called 'sprang', which are believed to have been made in he fifteenth century B.C., have been found on bodies, in frozen bogs in Scandinavia. They are made of a meshed fabric, much more elastic than woven material. The foundation loops out of which a 'sprang' fabric is built, are interlocked vertically instead of horizontally, as in a true-knitted fabric. Source: *History of Technology*, Singer, Holmyard, Hall and Williams (1957).

[20] Accounts of the Chapter of the Collegiate Church of SS. Peter and Wilfrid, Ripon, Yorkshire. Surtees Society.

[21] 4 Henry VII. C. 7.

[22] 5 & 6 Edward VI. C. 7.

A fashion note, in Stow, relating to Henry VIII tells us '. . . that by great chance, there came a payr of Spanish silk stockings from Spayne. . . . The phrase 'by great chance' emphasizes the fact that even for royalty, including Henry VIII, Spanish hand-knit stockings were something special and not easily obtainable.

Knitting is referred to in the earliest English comedy, 'Ralph Roister Doister'. Written and performed in Eton in 1534, it depicts a scene and there is a description of tired English working-girls at their assigned task in a home, trying to ward off sleep by singing:

Anno knits, Ribet sews and Madge spins
on the distaff.[23]

The classic story is told by Stow of the introduction of knitted worsted stockings, in England, in the year 1564:

In the yeare one thousand five hundred sixty and foure, William Rider, being an apprentice with Maister Thomas Burdett, at the Bridge Foote, over against Saint Magnus Church, chaunced to see a pair of knit worsted stockings, in the lodgings of an Italian merchant, that came from Mantua.
He borrowed these stockings, and caused other stockings to be made by *them*. And these were the first worsted stockings made in England.[24]

One would wish that the Chronicler, Stow, who was a member of the Merchant Taylors' Guild himself and probably also a maker of cut and sewn stockings, would have given more details and clarified the word 'them'. One may speculate that the knit worsted stockings were used as a model to copy from. The hand-knitters must have been highly experienced to have created the handicraft of knitting

[23] *Ralph Roister Doister:* Nicholas Udall (1534).
[24] John Stow: *The Annales, or General Chronicles of England* (1615).

worsted stockings from one single sample. They could have been 'decayed cap-knitters' or Huguenot refugees, members of the French Guild of Stocking Knitters, who had escaped from the persecutions in France and settled in Spitalfields.

Stow continued: 'Within a few years later, began the plenteous making both of kersey and woollen stockings, and so, in a short space, they waxed common.'

FIVE

'A Loome to Knit'

TRADITION has it that William Lee built his loom-to-knit while living in the Glebe House in Calverton, a low building abutting the road not too far from St. Wilfrid's Church. The parsonage consisted of a sitting-room and kitchen on the ground floor, with two chambers above. It would have been ample for a married pastor with a family but Lee, unmarried, used the Glebe House as a workroom in which he developed his invention.[1] With his younger brother, James, at his side he spent three years in trial and effort before he was able to knit coarse woollen stockings.

His plan was to produce a loom on which a stocking or a fabric could be knitted instead of woven. He would have hoped the invention would be for the good of the people, the commonweal and perhaps for himself. The Protestant ethic was not opposed to the pursuit of trade and such secular thoughts were not too far from the teachings of William Perkins—nor from Cambridge where he had observed fellow-students wearing knit nether-stocks, criticized as 'too fine for scholars'.

Conflicting thoughts about leaving the church and devoting his energies to the development of his loom may have turned him again to the message of William Perkins, whose injunction to persevere in a vocation did not prevent a lawful change of occupation:

> Change of vocation may be lawfully made . . . lawful, if for the publike good. Every man must judge that the particular calling in which God has placed him, to be the best of all callings for him . . . in service of God and the Commonweal.[2]

[1] G. Henson: *History of Frame-Work Knitting and Lace Trades* (1831).
[2] William Perkins: *Treatise of the Vocations* (1603).

We have no evidence of how the idea of a knitting machine first came to Lee, nothing to compare with the account that the inventor James Watt was to give two centuries later:

> I had gone for a walk on a Sabbath afternoon, thinking of the engine. Suddenly the idea came to my mind that as steam was an elastic body, it would rush in to a vacuum, and might be condensed without cooling the engine. The whole thing was arranged in my mind.[3]

Dr. Thoroton is the original source for the story that a woman was Lee's *deus ex machina*.

> At Calverton was born William Lee, who seeing a woman knit . . . created . . . a loom to knit.

Many traditional stories exist, with numerous variations, giving a motivation for Lee's invention. All have as a basic theme either love for a wife and child, or the desire to avenge an unrequited love. Elsmore, the British artist, tells one story, in a painting based on the legend that Lee was expelled from the university for marrying contrary to the statutes; his wife helped to support the family by knitting and Lee, watching her, got the idea of replacing hand-knitting by a machine so that his wife would no longer have to support the family by her efforts. The invention of the machine followed and Lee became wealthy, successful and honoured—a romantic story but quite untrue!

Writing in 1835, Gravener Henson, the economic historian, relates another traditional story current at that time with the frame-work knitters:

'Mr. Lee paid his addresses to a young woman in his neighbourhood, to whom, from some cause his attentions were not agreeable, or with more probability, it has been conjectured, she affected to treat him with negligence to ascertain her power over his affections. Whenever he paid his visits, she always took care to be busily engaged in knitting, and would pay no attention to his addresses. This

[3] Mirsky and Nevins: *The World of Eli Whitney* (1952).

account was pursued to such a harsh extent, and for so long a period, that the lover became disgusted, and he vowed to devote his future leisure, instead of dancing attendance upon a capricious woman, who treated his affections with cold neglect, in devising an invention that should effectually supersede her favourite employment of knitting, and he would show her how important he would be.

'So sedulous was Mr. Lee in his new occupation that he neglected everything for this new object of his attention, even his sacerdotal duties. In vain did his sweetheart endeavour to reclaim him. She found, too late, that she had carried her humour too far. All interests, all avocations, all affections were absorbed in his new pursuit, from which he imagined he should realize an immense fortune. His Curacy was despised, and at length, abandoned as beneath the notice of a person who had formed, in his imagination, such gigantic prospects.'

We know that Lee did, as Henson related, give up his sacerdotal duties. Though he may have imagined 'gigantic prospects' for his invention, he may also have hoped they would be for the 'good of the Commonweal'—a phrase of great significance in the obtaining of a patent as will be seen later.

John Blackner, a regional historian, gives a third version:[4]

'Lee was deeply smitten by a certain young woman of captivating charm, who conducted a knitting school, where she taught the young women of Nottingham the "arte and misterie" of hand-knitting. She was an excellent teacher, attracting pupils from all over the county, and waxed exceeding rich. When Lee made his advances she was always more interested in knitting stockings and teaching her pupils the art, than paying attention to the attempted caresses of her suitor. Lee thereupon determined to avenge himself. He would invent a machine. The object of his love would no longer have students, and would be compelled to close her school. He then proceeded to invent the loom, the

[4] John Blackner: *History of Nottingham* (1815).

young lady lost all her pupils, closed her school, and because of grief fell into a decline.'

This story if both the romantic attachment and the revenge motive, which are also a part of other traditional tales, are eliminated and the factor of the knitting school solely considered, may have the kernel of truth. That knitting schools were conducted in Elizabethan England by charming young ladies, and even by one of Lee's acquaintances, is true.

Nevertheless it is improbable that Lee, to average himself for being spurned, would have contrived to make the teaching of hand-knitting unprofitable by destroying its market, and that he would have invented a machine to accomplish this purpose.

In passing, it is interesting to note that 'to sette the poore to worke' by the establishment of knitting schools was the policy of the parish authorities, of which Lee was one, in carrying out the provisions of the Poor Laws. These were designed for pauper children, the aged, the weak, and the infirm so that they could be taught a trade for which knitting needles only were necessary, despite the fact that this policy was in disregard to the glut of hand-knitters of caps on the market.

In Norwich an order had been promulgated that 'a knitting-school dame[5] be provided in every parish, to sette the poore children and other poore to worke'.[6] In Norfolk the justices resolved 'that poore children be putte to schools to knittinge and spinning dames, the church-wardens and the overseers of the poore to pay the school-dames their wages, when the parents are not able'.[7]

In Leicester in 1591 the town contributed money 'to a certain Cheeseman, who undertook . . . to teach a competent number of women and men how to knit, and to hide nothing from them that belonged to the knowledge of the

---

[5] Knitting-school dame = a girl or woman who taught knitting in a school.
[6] Norwich Court Books: 1630.
[7] A. J. Armstrong: *History of the County of Norfolk* (1781).

said science'.[8] Further articles of agreement in 1592 between Cheeseman and the authorities included, '. . . the training of teachers was to teach Francis Newby and his wife the trade of knitting, spinning and dressing wool': Newby and his wife in turn were to give the oversight and teaching of thirty learners.

Leaving aside the wealth of romantic, improbable tales that grew up around the inventor, it is quite a possible assumption that Lee's interest in the art of knitting awoke and was kindled at Cambridge and had not remained merely a topic of conversation, but prompted him to experiment while still a young student. It was a fascinating occupation to form thread into loops and, with two little sticks of wood transform a ball of wool into a piece of elastic fabric. And was it not surprising that a stocking consisted of a single long thread? It is likely that he thought about the problem long before the end of his theological studies and carved wooden pins of various shapes or bent them out of wire and knitted with them.

He must have known the age-old method of weaving cloth by combining warp and weft, and how one could create fine and most intricate patterns with them. Why should it not be possible to construct a loom on which one could knit? He would, at first, hardly have thought of material gain but was irresistably attracted by the technical challenge.

After his return from Cambridge he continued his experiments on a larger scale. Nottingham as we have seen lay at the edge of the large Sherwood Forest which provided excellent wood, there was iron ore and coal, and the town was known for the craftsmanship and skill of its carpenters and locksmiths. The Rev. William Lee became a frequent visitor in their workshops and learnt to handle plane, file, and drill. They showed him many a trick of their trades, made useful suggestions and helped him with the most difficult jobs, but no doubt most of the work he did himself.

[8] E. M. Leonard: *Early History of English Poor Relief.*

With incredible patience he concentrated on the construction of the mechanism which he hoped would ultimately replace hand knitting pins. A large part of his inheritance was spent in this manner.

Lacking a record from the inventor's own pen to tell us how he went about designing his stocking frame, we have to rely on the tales of old framework knitters who passed the story on by word of mouth, from generation to generation. They were full of admiration for the inventor's genius and never tired of describing the difficulties he had to overcome. Two such old knitters, Mr. Hardys of Twisters Alley, Bunhill Row, London, who was ninety years old in 1790, and Mr. Woods of Godalming who died in Nottingham at the age of ninety-two, gave detailed accounts to the historian Gravener Henson of what they had been told when they were young apprentices. Henson's book, which was published in 1831, and the careful study of specimens of stocking frames which can be found in various museums, enable us to form an idea of the manner in which Lee must have set about constructing his machine.

When knitting by hand one holds a row of stitches on one needle, while one forms and gathers a new row with the other. In all probability young William had realized early on that the movements of this operation were far too complicated to be imitated mechanically. He had to find some method that avoided the difficult transfer of the stitches from one needle to the other. It was therefore not possible to design a machine with only two, three, four, or five needles, but each stitch had to have a needle of its own. And if the movement had to be as simple as possible, there was no alternative but to make the shape of the needles more complicated, so that they could take over a larger part of the knitting function.

He took a short piece of wire, about as thick as a small nail, and drilled a hole through it. Then he filed the end to a point and bent it back into a hook, which he hardened in a flame. Now he could press the point of the hook into the hole and when he let go it sprang back. One could form loops and stitches with this little tool, but they would not slide over the closed hook and caught where the point fitted in the hole. He therefore made the hooks longer and thinner and instead of a hole, he scraped a slot with a triangular file. When this effort failed, he hammered the wire flat and bent the edges up, again without much success. After many attempts and a great deal of spoilt wire, it occurred to him to use a chisel for cutting the slot into which he could now press the point of the hook. His friend, the locksmith, or perhaps the clock- or gunsmith helped him to harden the

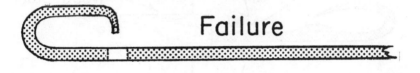

Failure

Success

hook and so the spring needle was perfected which we still use today to knit the sheerest stockings.

The next job was to manufacture as many needles as there were stitches in the widest part of the circumference of the stocking. But Lee soon gave up the idea of building a circular machine. It proved far more complicated than had appeared at first sight. The needles had to be arranged in a straight line. Lee cut a series of small wooden blocks, each $1\frac{1}{2}''$ long, and hammered 12 needles into each block. He then screwed these blocks next to each other on to a frame, so that all the needles were arranged in a horizontal row.

Then he cut vertical slots into the wooden blocks, always one slot between two needles, into which he fitted flat strips

S.Q.—F

of thin sheet metal, so that he could slide them up and down.
We now call these metal strips sinkers. Each sinker had a
small nose, and if a thread was laid across the needles and
the sinkers were pushed down, one after another, the noses
caught the thread and formed it into loops. With a comb

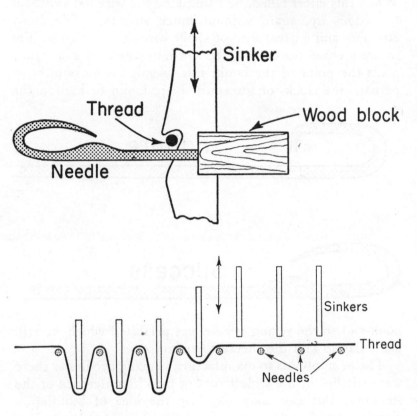

he pushed the loops under the needle hooks, and held them
there by pressing the row of hooks down with a bar. Then
he used the comb to push the previous row of stitches over
the needle hooks and thus, with skill and patience, knitted
a fresh row.

But one needed three hands to operate this instrument,
which gave Lee the idea to lengthen the sinkers and fit them
with hinges on to levers or jacks. This made it possible not

only to drop and raise the sinkers, but also to push them forwards and back and so dispense with the comb. Now, unfortunately, the bar that closed the needle hooks was in the way and he had to move the whole press unit to the front of the machine. That was a complication but it had the advantage that it gave him room to fix the axle, which supported the jacks, on to a slide, giving the sinkers perfect freedom of movement.

In order to push the sinkers, one after the other, down between the needles and so shape the thread into loops, he

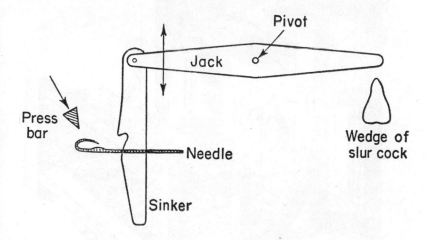

invented the slur-cock. It was a wedge-shaped piece of iron which pushed the back ends of the jacks upwards and therefore the sinkers, which were hinged on the front end of the jacks, downwards between the needles. Pulled by a rope, the slur-cock travelled from side to side, right across the width of the row of jacks, sinkers and needles, comparable to the shuttle of a weaving loom, only much slower. Lee guided the rope over a wheel, which he connected with two foot pedals, so that he could now drop the sinkers with his feet, freeing the hands for other operations.

Step by step he advanced, one improvement logically leading to the next. The slide was mounted on small rollers

continued on page 70

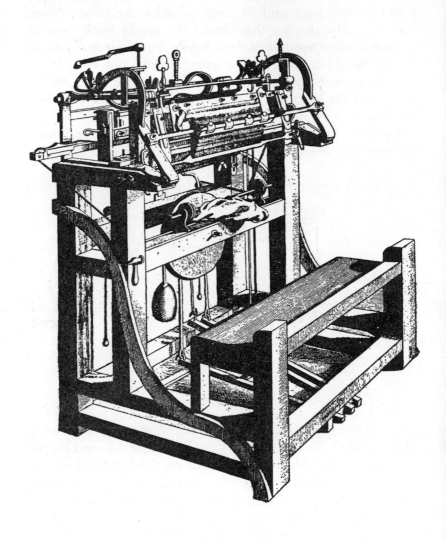

The stocking frame was constructed remotely like a weaving loom. The framework was made of solid wood beams which carried the mechanism made from wrought iron, steel needles and steel springs. It had a bench for the workman to sit on and several foot pedals.

A weaving loom used warp, i.e. a large number of threads arranged vertically through which the shuttle passed horizontally, thus tying in the weft with the warp. By contrast, the stocking frame only used one thread which unwound from a bobbin. With two of the foot pedals one could turn the large centre wheel to the left or to the right. This wheel pulled the rope to which the slur-box was attached. If the workman presses the right pedal down, the wheel turns clockwise, pulling the slur-cock from left to right. This pushed the far end of the jacks up and brought the sinkers down, thus forming a row of loops from left to right.

The workman then pulled the sinkers towards him, pushing the loops under the needle hooks. Then he pressed a third foot pedal which brought down the presser bar and closed the needle hooks. The fabric hanging on the needle shafts was then pushed forward over the needle hooks and 'knocked off'. This completed the knitting operation.

The fabric now hanging on the newly formed row of loops was pushed back to the foot of the needle shafts, a fresh length of thread was laid across the row of needles from right to left and the operation repeated, this time in the opposite direction. The workman pressed the left foot pedal down making the slur-cock travel to the left.

and became a carriage, the presser bar was connected to another foot pedal relieving the hands still further. Each jack was supported by a steel spring to hold it neatly in position instead of having to rely on friction. And so, after many years of hard work, emerged in 1589 the first stocking frame, an instrument much more complicated than a watch, the most intricate and wonderful machine the world had ever seen and William Lee was its sole inventor. The method of forming knitted stitches which he conceived was so perfect that the most modern high-speed fully fashioned stocking machines in use today still employ the same technique.

To appraise Lee's achievement, one needs to measure the technical environment of his time. In the middle of the sixteenth century mechanical science was not advanced in England. Largely, the stimuli for its beginnings came from ideas brought into the land by the Dutch, Flemish, and French refugees who fled from religious persecution, as well as from the wares from distant lands brought in by the English mercantile marine. William Felkin, a nineteenth-century economic historian talks of 'bringing in materials from distant parts for future manufactures . . . the supplying new means of comfort and enjoyment to the people', and relates it to the 'stimulation of freedom of thought, prompting the prolific brain of the inventor to new discoveries'.[9] A. L. Rowse, the twentieth-century historian of the sixteenth, correlates with the expansion of economic horizons the growth of inventive ingenuity. He stresses the influence of the new religious doctrines, '. . . the prime discoverers of the English past and present, the chroniclers, the topographers, surveyors and map-makers, were a strongly Protestant lot. Lovers of the past . . . they were looking back into the past for support, but, support regarding the new uncharted course.'[10]

To chart the new, some sought to discover ways to peace

[9] William Felkin: *A History of the Machine-Wrought Hosiery and Lace Manufacturers* (1867).
[10] A. L. Rowse: *William Shakespeare* (1965).

and security in their immediate present, in terms of loyalty to their Queen and country. Hugh Platt, in the *Jewel House of Art and Nature* (1594), listing his works on practical devices and useful contrivances, urges that to their value of 'something of profit to the commonwealth' there be added the inventions of 'choice wits' for the enrichment of England and, thereby, to move toward the elimination of the menace of Spain.[11] Intrinsic in the fear of Spain was the threat of its Catholic doctrine, which stimulated the inventive capacity of Sir John Napier to create a burning mirror for destruction of ships and an armoured chariot, as 'profitabill & necessary in their dayes for the defense of this Iland & withstanding of strangers, enemies of God's truth and religion'.[12]

As the Elizabethan's loyalty was becoming less directed to his town and his guild and more to his Queen, with his respect for the power of the Crown, his thoughts were turning to overseas enterprise as a means of national strength. William Lee's turn of mind may well have identified with another fellow-preacher, Richard Hakluyt, whose college degrees from Oxford predated his from Cambridge by some eight years. The year of Lee's invention, 1589, was that of the publication of Hakluyt's 'Principal Navigations', which showed his interest in both secular and religious duties, and his quest by precept and example to teach his countrymen the value and profit of overseas enterprise.[13] Lee may have been impressed with the Queen's responsiveness to Hakluyt, who gained her favour and patronage for his 'Discourse of Western Planning'; this was a plea urging that North American colonization through trade projects should be encouraged in order to prosper the commercial and artisan classes.

Hakluyt also stressed that in colonization piety and profits went hand in hand; exports of English cloth would grow, and this increase be the result of teaching the natives in colonized lands to wear Christian raiment. It is noticeable

---

[11] L. B. Wright: *Middle Class Culture in Elizabethan England* (1935).
[12] Ibid.   [13] Ibid.

that the fighting seamen, Drake, Hawkins, and the Merchant companies which were formed in London to push trade to distant parts of the world, were strong Protestants.[14]

Later when Lee came to London and was concerned about the acceptance of his machine he may well have been both interested and encouraged by the success of another invention. This was a corn-grinding mill invented in 1594 by two alien Dutchmen. Though windmills had been employed for ages in grinding corn, this invention of Jacob Senoy and George Fine was recommended by the Lord Mayor and the Aldermen, 'it would serve for City if besieged, or in times of frost when the mills go not'.[15] Significant was the claim for it that it would grind a greater amount of corn in a shorter time, and the knitting-loom inventor may have pondered this principle when looking for a similar success.

The 'common' pin of modern times evolved from a harvesting procedure. Its earliest ancestor was the prickle-of-thorns, picked by the poor women of Wales and known as 'pin draen'. In 1543 England imported pins from France and later learnt the art of making them from the alien Netherlanders. When the English makers petitioned against further importation from the Continent, the Netherlands merchants criticized their new skill: 'the pins, gross and stiff, not so fine for linen . . . and, as yet they be only half-masters, and ought not so soon exclude their teachers'.[16] None the less, utility and cheapness for the English product won out and by proclamation on December 29, 1564, further importation was prohibited.

If Lee was aware of the English pinners claim, 'that by new invention, learned of the strangers . . . two men would point more pins than 100 could formerly do' . . . again on the premise of faster-and-more he would have high hopes of royal recognition of his invention. For through constant experimentation over several years on his first machine in

[14] G. M. Trevelyan: *English Social History* (1944).
[15] S. J. Burn: *History of Foreign Protestant Refugees settled in England* (1846). [16] Ibid.

the Glebe House, he achieved 500 to 600 loops instead of the 100 loops formed in a minute by skilful hand-knitting.[17]

The common sewing needle was brought from India after the discovery of the route by the Cape of Good Hope. Before its introduction sewing was performed in the method used by shoe makers. One Englishman gleaned the secret of the needle, its eye, and after the inventor discovered the method of punching an eye in steel needles, he realized a large profit from it by monopolizing the secret.[18]

News of inventions and secrets giving great profit will have inspired Lee. Devices of all kinds were in the air, such as Hugh Platt's which included: 'How to keep meats from spoiling', 'How to keep fresh water from putrefaction'; in 1594 there was inventive progress indeed when he contributed 'How to brew good and wholsom Beere without anie Hoppes at all'.[19] Cyprian Lucar, we learn from *A Treatise named Lucar Solace*, achieved before 1590 a fire engine in the form of a 'kinde of squirt, made to hold an hoggeshead of water'.[20] Many of the so-called inventions were merely collections of recipes for making desirable products, ranging from coloured inks to preserving wines, and without benefit of scientific method.

Of course the day of the Industrial Revolution proper, with the development of machines and the application of power to operate them, was still very much in the future. Progress in medieval industry and in crafts took the form of a growth of manual skills. Progress in the introduction of machinery lagged because inventions were looked upon with distrust.[21]

This was a point perhaps that inventors like William Lee did not fully grasp. In his day what was not understood was feared. Superstition was still rampant and women were burned at the stake, accused of witchcraft.[22] Even in high

---

[17] Felkin: op. cit.   [18] Ibid.

[19] Wright: op. cit. See Charles Elton's *William Shakespeare, His Family and Friends* (1904), who quotes from Platt.   [20] Wright: op. cit.

[21] Sir John Clapham: *Economic History of Britain*, Cambridge (1957).

[22] J. Orange: *History of Nottingham* (1840).

places there was traffic with astrologers; courtiers like the Earl of Leicester, Adrian Gilbert, and Secretary Walsingham consulted John Dee, distinguished mathematician and astronomer who cast Queen Elizabeth's horoscope to select the most auspicious date for her coronation.[23] In turn, some of the handicraftsmen in their estimate of Lee's loom, may have characterized it as the devilry of astrologer and alchemist.

While the spirit of inquiry increased in the sixteenth century, some theological writers in alarm warned the public that 'God would resent meddling in his secret affairs'. William Vaughan violently condemned the 'perseverance of the common man, in ferreting out the mysteries reserved for God'. He voiced his displeasure 'in man's curiosity into prying into God's nature'. Abraham Fleming, author of works on earthquakes, writing in 1588 even opposed 'too much exploration into natural phenomena'.[24]

Apart from obstacles of this kind, was the social attitude of Elizabethan England such as to favour the product of Lee's invention? To an item of dress, less utilitarian than pins and needles and other practical contrivances, the people's response might have been of two extremes. Among those who admired the Queen for her learning, political wisdom, and concern for her subjects, the example of her splendid appearance and spectacular dress would tend to encourage the trend towards fashion and finery both at the Court and for the rising commonalty. On the other hand, the fanatical Puritans looked on the growing ostentation in women's dress with suspicion, and to them additions to her wardrobe would be regarded as symbols of extravagance, folly, and frivolity. Knit stockings for both sexes would be judged as a 'useless' commodity and thus the work of a 'sinner'.

For many the question of finery in dress was closely linked to that of social status. Though Elizabethan society was less rigid in structure than that of some other European countries,

[23] Edith Sitwell: *The Queens and the Hive* (1962).   [24] Wright: op. cit.

it was in no sense equalitarian. Shakespeare, for instance, found men and women of every class interesting to him but he held 'degree' as the basis of human welfare. Expressed in *Troilus and Cressida*,

> *The heavens themselves, the planets and this centre*
> *Observe degree, priority, and place . . .*

As Lord Burghley, Queen Elizabeth's principal adviser, put it the Elizabethan age was an 'ambitious age'. He told his son Robert, who later succeeded him as Royal Treasurer, 'Everything depended on knowing the right people'. Further, 'Be sure to keep some great man as thy friend, compliment him often . . . and if thou have some cause to bestow some gratuity, let it be something as may daily be in his sight'.[25]

A 'mild' though influential Anglican, Lord Burghley who was no Puritan expressed himself both in a supporting statute and in his personal view against extravagance in the apparel of those below the obviously rich.[26]

In the devotional writings of the day, Thomas Nash in *Christ's Teares Over Jerusalem* (1593) also deplores the sin of 'gorgeous attire' that threatens to destroy differences in social status:

> . . . for wanton disguising thyself against kind, and digressing from the plainness of thy ancestors, . . . shameful . . . that not any in thee live but above their ability and birth . . . that the outward habit should yield in thee no difference of persons.

William Harrison also stated the case of the excesses of fashion, in 1587:

> You shall not see any so disguised as are my country-men, how much cost is bestowed upon our bodies, and how little upon our souls . . . then must the long seams of our hose be set by a plumb line . . . their farthingales,

---

[25] Conyers Read: *Mr. Secretary Cecil and Queen Elizabeth* (1955).
[26] Ibid.

and diversely coloured nether stocks of silk, and such-like, whereby, their bodies are rather deformed than commended.[27]

And Thomas Middleton (1604) in his satire on *The Portrait of a Dandy* painted fashion-change as out-distancing the past but still unacceptable:

> His breeches were full, as deep as the roadway between London and Winchester . . . so large . . . that within a twelve month he might very well put all his lands in them . . . they differ so from our fashioned hose in the country, and from his father's old gascoins, that his back part seemed to us like a monster.

A more objective historian observed, 'All manners of attire came first into the city and country from the Court',[28] and Lee's plans for the product of his loom may have turned to an item of dress much prized in Elizabethan times—gloves. At the Queen's Progress to Cambridge University, Christ's College Master, Edward Hawford, had presented a 'paire to Her Majestie, which she handled fondly'.[29] And from Christ's, for important personages as important gifts, one pair was bestowed on Lord Burghley and one pair on Lord Robert Dudley, who for many years was a suitor of the Queen. Similarly as a peace-offering to a certain Dr. Neile, to placate him for charging the college with fourteen 'abuses' requiring reform, went one pair of gloves, which in 1586 cost 10 shillings.[30]

Originally imported from France and Spain, gloves later received the Queen's grant in the form of a licence to Andrea de Loos for making 20,000 pelts yearly, which was not unattractive to her 'for he payd Her Majestie 20 shillings per 100 pelts'. Objections to the licence came in Lee's time,

---

[27] Rev. William Harrison: *Description of the Island of Great Britain* 2nd edition (1587).
[28] Fynes Morrison: *Itinerary* (1617).
[29] Francis Peck: *Desiderata Curiosa* (1732).
[30] J. Peile: *Christ's College* (1900).

'it will overthrow the new trade of glovers, making gloves of shepe and lam skynnes, late much growen up within London and other Cytyes'. The plea and complaint from the English glove-makers who, 'to have them vendible (gloves), doe perfume them, put them in diverse colours and sortes of trimmings with lace', was that the new home industry should not be exposed to the competition of a foreign licensee. Moreover, the '*new* trade of gloves made in the realm' would have been uniquely free of any problem of displacement of craftsmen, in its trade enterprise.[31]

The arbitrary and capricious awarding of licence-grants was to provoke many such protests. During the Queen's reign members of the Privy Council were favoured by grants of numerous licences and monopolies. A licence was granted to Lord Hunsdon in 1589 to transport 20,000 pieces of woollen cloth to Europe, during a six-month period. At the same time, not to disfavour Secretary Walsingham a licence was granted to him for the exportation of 30,000 cloths, over a three-year period. Another grant of a licence was made to Lord Burghley and several other members of the Privy Council to build salt-works at various points along the sea-coast. This would have resulted in a national mono-poly for the production and sale of salt throughout the kingdom, and the grantees could have raised prices at will. Unfortunately for Burghley and his associates, but fortun-ately for the people, the plan ended in failure.[32]

The granting of patents and monopolies was also the prerogative of the Queen, and she followed largely a policy of bestowing these privileges upon her personal favourites and courtiers who were also important officers. In lieu of salaries she frequently made grants to minor officials, clerks, and personal pensioners. While it was her prerogative to grant to favoured individuals, it was also her prerogative to withhold.[33]

In 1592 Richard Young was one of several courtiers who

[31] Burn: op. cit.   [32] Conyers Read: op. cit.
[33] W. H. Price: *English Patents of Monopoly* (1906).

received the sole licence and authority for making, selling, or importing starch throughout the entire realm. In the case of the starch monopoly the courtiers who successively enjoyed it had been in debt to the Queen and she hoped to reimburse herself by helping them at the expense of her subjects. In such licences the advantage financially often went to the Crown by the payment of what were called 'rents'; the payment of these 'rents' often resulted in the division of the profits of an enterprise with the Royal Treasury. It was in fact an Elizabethan device for tax-collection, a practice adopted by the ministerial arm in its system of internal administration.[34]

Quite unaware of course of the Queen's ambivalence in the administration of the law, William Lee may well have been encouraged and hopeful of receiving his patent, under a policy in vogue prior to 1601:

> If any man, out of his wit, industry, or endeavour, find out anything beneficial for the Commonwealth, or bring any new invention, which every subject of the realm may use . . . her Majesty is pleased to grant him a privilege . . . to use the same for himself, for a certain time.

It would seem that the inventor's 'loome-to-knitte' would come well within the scope of such a policy, for '*out of his wit . . . and endeavour*' he had invented the loom '*beneficial to the commonwealth*'.

Full of the brightest hopes Lee had every right to seek out the Queen, confident she would '*grant him a privilege . . . for a certain time*'.

---

[34] S. T. Bindoff: *Tudor England* (1950).

SIX

Hawkers, Guilds, and Stockings

Such wind as scatters young men throughout the world,
To seek their fortunes further than at home,
Where small experience grows . . .[1]

THE momentous, soul-searching decision to abandon his curacy at Calverton and carry his machine to London must have been determined by Lee sometime between the years 1589, which historical record accepts as the date of his invention, and 1590. He took with him his youngest brother James, then only some ten years old, who had kept house with him at Calverton and who was trained in the working of his loom.

Understandable indeed was the perturbation within the Lee family not only at the departure of two of its members from an approved and ordered way of life but for a goal that will have appeared illusory and worthless, running quite counter to the ways of God.

Yet for the inventor it will have been a God-given mission and as he and James stood on the deck of the small vessel carrying them into London, and for the first time his eyes set sight upon the great city lying before him, he will have trusted to God's will to carry them both through all vicissitudes. Little can he have realized, then, the bitter experiences lying ahead.

When he arrived with his precious knitting-loom at the mouth of the estuary of the Thames, it was still forty miles to London Bridge. Sailing upstream he will have passed Blackwall from where, later in 1606, John Smith set sail in three small vessels to establish the first permanent colony in

[1] Shakespeare: *The Taming of the Shrew.*

America. The boat will have passed Deptford, where Queen Elizabeth drove to greet Sir Francis Drake when he returned from his three-year voyage round the world with a heavy prize of captured Spanish treasure.

Reaching London Bridge, top-heavy with houses, at the Bankside Gate the two brothers passed the open space where the Crown set up pikes impaled with the heads of convicted traitors . . . a most gruesome greeting. Lee might have made arrangements to leave his knitting-frames on the boat for a few days until he found living quarters for himself and his brother James, and a workshop where he could set up his loom.

In many respects London was still a medieval town, bounded by a defensive wall, guarded by the Tower, with its centre the great Cathedral Church of St. Paul. Beginning with the Tower on the east, the wall described an arc of which the Thames was the hub, extending to the River Fleet on the west, a distance of over two miles in circumference.[2] The wall itself was pierced by nine gates from which roads extended on to the country, two of them, Cripplegate and Bishopgate, leading in the general direction of Bunhill Fields where Lee was to set up his machine.

Along the Thames riverside were the Palaces of Savoy and White-Hall; the homes of the nobility were practically continuous as far as Westminster Hall. London was also the city of bankers and promoters, the great merchant adventurers who had risen to prosperity and influence as traders: at a lower level were the mercers, haberdashers, and wool merchants, meeting the widening social needs of the people. In addition there were refugees, thousands of whom had fled from persecutions on the Continent . . . mechanics, artisans, hawkers, apprentices, and nobility too. Adding to the hubbub were civil servants, army officers with their varying degrees of authority, and the soldiers and sailors who, not yet returned to their homes after the destruction of the Armada, had heard the Queen make her famous speech at Tilbury Camp.[3]

[2] Ashley H. Thorndyke: *London*.   [3] John Nichols: *Progresses* (1708).

10. Memorial window to William Lee at Christ's College, Cambridge.

11. William Cecil, First Baron Burghley (1520–98), Lord High Treasurer to Queen Elizabeth. Artist unknown.

The population of London at that time was nearly a quarter of a million and it must have taken William Lee, fresh from peaceful Calverton, many weeks before he became accustomed to the noise and tumult, the cries of the carters, boatmen, and street-hawkers filling the air. The houses and the shops opened on the streets. Shopping and bargaining, marketing and visiting were carried on largely on the public thoroughfare. A typical shop of the sixteenth century consisted of a single room on the level of the street, upon which opened a large unglazed window, the shutter letting down to form a counter. By contrast the goldsmiths' shops displayed their wares in windows with covered glass. While some goods were displayed in the open window to catch the eye of the possible purchaser, the shopkeeper's wife or daughter was not above sitting in the doorway to act as an additional attraction.[4]

In those days, and as far back as the twelfth century, the names of the streets often indicated the nature of the market found there: Bread Street, Milk Street, and Fish Street, all had rows of stalls in front of the small shops. The ironmongers concentrated on Iron-Monger Street, the carpenters and cabinetmakers on Wood Street, and The Poultry (still so named) was the centre for fowl and game.[5] Lee will have noted how every shop had its own signboard. The Mercer, deriving his sign from Mercator, displayed a map of the world; the Haberdasher showed the Queen's Arms; the Linen-draper pictured the hare and hound, and the Woollen-draper the fleece.

A number of new crafts were established by the refugee aliens in the city, making goods in imitation of foreign wares. Potters in Lambeth, for instance, were making earthenware dishes just like the Italian majolica-ware. Venetian glass was blown in a glass-refractory, erected by Jacopo Verselino, in Crutched Friars in 1571; the glass he blew was in great demand and of excellent quality.[6]

[4] Thorndyke: op. cit.   [5] Stow: *Survey of London* (1630).
[6] Craik and Macfarlane: *History of England* (1846).
S.Q.—G

Many hosiers had their shops on the London Bridge, and had Lee thought to stop at a shop on the Bridge Foot over against St. Magnus's Church to inquire about the shop of Master Burdett, reputed to have been the hosier who introduced the first worsted stockings hand-knit in England, he would have learned that Master Burdett no longer conducted the shop and his old apprentice was now in charge. As in the past, he would have been told the story of many changes:

> The hosiers of old-time had their shops in Hosier Lane, near until Smithfield. But, they had since removed to Cordwainers Street, the upper part thereof by Bow Church, and last of all into Birchover Lane, by Cornhill.
>
> Men of trades and sellers of wares in this city, have oftentimes since changed their places, as they have found to their best advantage. For, whereas mercers and haberdashers used to keep their shoppes on West Cheape, of later times they held them on London Bridge, where a goodly number still remain.[7]

If he had stopped at any one of the Hosier shops on London Bridge, William Lee would have learned that three major guilds contended for the right and privilege of selling 'hosen and stockings'. There was constant conflict and jurisdictional disputes between the Merchant Drapers, the Merchant Taylors, and the Merchant Haberdashers as to who should have the exclusive right of selling this increasingly important article of wearing apparel . . . stockings. In 1367 the selling of cut and sewn hose had become a separate trade from the making.[8] In 1502 Henry VII granted to the Merchant Taylors' Guild 'the exclusive monopoly of working, cutting or making men's apparel within the City of London' and this was to 'include all types of cut and sewn stockings'.[9]

---

[7] Stow: op. cit.
[8] C. M. Clode: *Early History of the Merchant Taylors* (1888).
[9] Rev. A. H. Johnson: *History of the Worshipful Company of Drapers of London* (1914).

But after 1530, under Henry VIII the Drapers, jealous of the exclusive monopoly granted to the Taylors, demanded and also secured the right of making and selling stockings at retail.[10]

William Lee was to discover later that another guild, the Weavers Company, claimed jurisdiction over his right to make loom-knit stockings, separate and distinct from his right of selling them.[11] Among the shopkeepers, not only the drapers, the tailors, and the haberdashers but also the hosiers in turn would vociferously claim the right to sell his product at retail.

Through the course of the centuries, craft guilds had taken to themselves the function of policing the price and quality of merchandise, both at wholesale and at consumer level.[12] It was the aim of the different guilds to ensure that the buyer actually received what he supposed he was buying. This right was protected under many royal statutes.

Walking along the Bridge with James and listening to the cries of apprentices and shopkeepers of 'What d'ye lack? What d'ye lack? . . .' William Lee probably decided it was impolitic at that time to talk to any of the shopkeepers who sold stockings. He will have perceived all too soon how sharply he would be in competition with hosiers, drapers, haberdashers, and mercers, and all who sold hand-knit worsted stockings as well as the cut and sewn; if his frame-work machine knitted in London as it did in Calverton, his loom-knit stockings faced great antagonisms.

> *Then into London towne I did me hye*
> *of all the lande it beareth the pryse;*
> *Then to the 'Cheape' I began me drawne*
> *Where much People I saw, for to stande.*

> *One offered me velvet, silke and lawne*
> *And other taketh me by the hande.*
> *'Here is Parys thread, the finest in the lande'.*

---

[10] Francis Consitt: *London Weavers' Company* (1933).
[11] J. A. Froude: *History of England* (1867).   [12] Stow: op. cit.

84 STOCKINGS FOR A QUEEN

Then went I forth to London stone
Throughout all coninge street,
Drapers much cloth me offered anone . . .[13]

So John Lydgate described the London scene. Though 'London Lickpenny' was written before the middle of the fifteenth century, the scenes the poet described were as true when Lee paid his first visit to the 'Cheape' as when Lydgate himself walked along that street. The 'Cheape' of Elizabethan England was the Regent Street of a later day. The 'Golden Chepe' of the merchants was a broad parade on the west side of a fine set of houses called Goldsmith's Row. There were by count fifty-two shops, concerning which an Italian had written:

> They were so rich and full of silver vessels, great and small, that in all the shops of Milan, Rome, Venice, and Florence, put together, I do not think there are to be found so many, nor of the magnificence to be seen in London.[14]

At the far end of the 'Cheape' Lee will have encountered the 'monumental sublimity' of St. Paul's. Merchants of every nation assembled in the Middle Aisle of the Cathedral, St. Paul's Walk as it was called, to procure bills of exchange, to hire shipping, to learn of the sailing of a particular vessel; gathering together to acquire commercial information, to make contracts, to enjoy gossip, to see and be seen.[15] Here also the fashionable tailor took his order, jotted down the measurements for cut and sewn as well as hand-knit worsted stockings. 'Milan-silk' stockings, hand-knit and described as being 'twice as strong as ours' and 'very massive', were then being offered to the curious. In a later day in Italy the Italian merchant was to offer Italian loom-knit stockings, claiming them 'as good as the English'.

---

[13] John Lydgate: *London Lickpenny* (1370–1451).
[14] Stow: op cit.
[15] R. J. Mitchell and M. D. R. Leys: *History of the English People* (1950).

An impecunious young blade, a soldier returned from France, his sword or dagger available for any adventure— a youngest son bored with his studies at the Inner Temple —all might gather at St. Paul's to see what Fortune offered them or what they could find to suit their particular talents. And in an open stall a bookseller would be offering at 3d. *A Balleting Silk-Weaver*, *The History of the London Prentice*, *The Merchant Taylors Renown*, books catering for Lee's changing thoughts as he turned less to religious literature and more to the new world of trade.

If Lee turned north from Cheapside, he would have walked past Gresham's Royal Exchange, with its Bourse on the main floor and the 'Curious Pawne' on the upper floor.

For in costly toys, silk stockings, cambric and lawne,
Here is a choice, full plenty, in the Curious Pawne.[16]

The building of the Royal Exchange by Sir Thomas Gresham was started in 1567 and took three years to finish.[17] It was a massive quadrangle with walks on the ground floor for the merchants, many of whom now ceased to transact their business in the Middle Aisle of St. Paul's. The interior was spaced out into 'walks' where members would be pretty sure to meet the merchants of any particular trade. There was the Clothiers' Walk, the Silk-Men's Walk, and a walk for practically every type of goods sold in the city.

In January 1571, attended by a splendid train the Queen repaired to the Bourse, visiting every part, and 'caused proclamation to be made by sound of trumpet, that henceforth it should bear the name of the Royal Exchange'. The promotion was successful and from that time the shops of the Exchange became the favourite resort of fashionable customers of both sexes.[18]

---

[16] Stow: op. cit.
[17] Holinshed: *Chronicles*.
[18] Lucy Aikin: *Memoirs of the Court of Elizabeth* (1818).

Gresham's Royal Exchange was destroyed in the Great London Fire of 1666. Divines of that day pronounced the catastrophe a judgment upon the avarice and unfair dealings of the merchants and shopkeepers, and upon the pride, prodigality and luxury of the purchasers and idlers who patronized it. Some Puritans saw in every natural phenomenon and cataclysm the hand of the Lord.

Travelling north from London Bridge to Cheapside and on to Bishopsgate, and passing through the old London Wall, was a distance of about three miles. Outside Bishopsgate lay the general area called 'Petty Fraunce' where from early times colonies of Frenchmen, refugees from political and religious persecutions, had settled.[19] These French refugees were to play a vital part in Lee's life.

To the west of Bishopsgate lay Cripplegate Parish, facing which was an area called Bunhill Fields. Here, Lee rented a small tenement where he planned to set up his loom on the ground floor, leaving sleeping and living quarters for himself and James on the upper floor.[20]

To avoid possible antagonisms, William Lee may have had a definite reason for locating his shop in the open country far from London Bridge or Cheapside, and well away from other hosiers or shops where cut and sewn or hand-knit worsted stockings were sold.

Not yet erased from the memory of this man of peace were perhaps the murmurings in Calverton about 'taking away bread from the family of honest craftsmen'.

---

[19] Stow: op. cit.
[20] G. Henson: *History of Frame-Work Knitting and Lace Trades* (1831).

SEVEN

Patents and Patronage

AT that moment when William Lee set up his loom in the small tenement in Bunhill Fields his perspective in time was limited to the immediate. He was impatient to seek the Queen for royal aid and the grant of a monopoly patent.

Grants of sole powers, rights, and advantages were usually secured to their possessors by 'letters patent' under the Royal Seal. For the document the recipient paid 6s. 8d., a nominal charge made for any document. Patents were originally issued for 10 years; later the term was increased to 20–30 years.

Without qualms of conscience the Queen, for instance, granted to Sir Walter Raleigh an exclusive licence 'for keeping of taverns and retailing of wines throughout England'. Abuses arising from this monopoly were complained of to Parliament as late as 1624, that 'if an inn-keeper set up a new post, unless he met the terms and payment of licence fees, even exorbitant ones, he was sued at Westminster'.

Apparently, patents issued to Court favourites included applicants who did not even claim to be the 'first introducers' of 'new arts'; invention was conveniently accepted as covering first importation of manufacturing processes from abroad, such as alum, glass, and paper.[1] The earliest recorded application for a patent was for 'introducing a new art' into England, and was granted to George Cobham in 1562. He was a relative of Sir Henry Cobham, former Ambassador to Spain, which may well have smoothed the way for his application. The patent was for a dredging machine, granted as a 'reward of diligent travail' . . . thus 'to give encourage-

[1] S. T. Bindoff: *Tudor England* (1950).

ment to others'.[2] Mechanical patents for meeting urgent needs, such as the draining of the Fens which was essential for low-lying areas, were issued with little delay.

Lee's invention could not claim this urgency. Indeed as an inventor whose machine displaced manpower, so interfering with an existing trade by putting his neighbour to a disadvantage, he might well not be considered a person who deserved encouragement of any kind.[3] The economic climate of the sixteenth and early seventeenth centuries was in sympathy with those who objected to the introduction of any 'ingine' which through its operation 'took the bread out of the mouth of some handicraft man'.

This hostile attitude was to acquire teeth in laws passed to forbid the use of labour-saving devices. One of the early attempts to stifle technological progress was in the clothing industry, which employed more people than any other. Prior to the reign of Henry VIII, after cloth had been woven, cleaned, thickened, and felted in water, it was given a nap by a hand-process with teasels—the heads of a flower such as a thistle covered with stiff leaves. During Henry's reign, machines called gig-mills for raising the nap of cloth first came into use. This progress was of short duration for in 1551, in the reign of Edward VI, parliament passed an Act 'for putting down of "gygy milles"'.[4] It was claimed that the gig-mills, known as 'machines of iron' were 'prejudical to the quality of the cloth' and 'the true draperie of the realm was impaired'. In reality, the basic objection was to the displacement of hand-labour by machine.

The prohibition of the use of gig-mills continued during the reign of Elizabeth, even imposing for its use a 'pain for forfeit' of £5.[5] But clearly the clothmakers continued to use the gig-mills in circumvention of the law for in 1597 a monopoly privilege was issued to Roger Binion and William

[2] Sir John Clapham: *Economic History of Britain* (1957).
[3] W. Cunningham: *Growth of English Industry and Commerce* (1910 Edition). [4] 5 & 6 Edward VI. C. 7.
[5] Craik and Macfarlane: *History of England* (1846).

Bennett for 'the collection of forfeitures' relating to the Act. In effect this permitted the making of arrangements for payment of 'anticipatory fines' which made the law practically null and void.[6]

In the records of the Cloth-Makers Booke for January 21, 1560, another instance is reported where the owners of weaving looms were disinclined to encourage more efficient methods of production.[7] The Court of Assistants of the Cloth-Workers Guild were waited upon by a Venetian inventor who exhibited a labour-saving device for the fulling of broadcloths, and 'for a consideration' offered to teach 'this feate of workmanship'. But, 'in the opinion of certain of the most expert men of the company', who were brought to see the device '. . . it would be a great decaye to the company' . . . ' whereupon the Master and the Wardens gave the sayd stranger great thanks, and also XX shillings, in money towards his charge and parted'. Twenty shillings was the price to save the company's 'decaye' from the threat of labour-saving.

Along with the granting of patents, another evil of the Elizabethan government and a hindrance to industrial progress was the system of granting monopolies. Monopolies differed from patents in that they were trade privileges given to certain individuals, or groups of individuals, who had the exclusive right 'to buy and sell . . . to import and export and otherwise deal in and control the distribution of certain articles or services'. We have seen some examples of this in an earlier chapter.

In 1601 the exclusive right and prerogative of the Queen to grant monopolies and patents was seriously questioned in Parliament. Lists of monopolies that had been granted during the reign of Elizabeth were handed about from member to member. The Queen's defence showed her characteristic deviousness:

[6] 36 Elizabeth C. 11.
[7] George Unwin: *Industrial Organization in the 15th and 16th centuries* (1904).

That my grants shall be made grievances to my people, and oppressions, to be privileged under the colour of our patents, our princely dignity shall not suffer it. And if my princely dignity have been abused, I hope God shall not lay their blame upon my charge. And though you may have mightier and wiser Princes, you never have had nor shall have any that shall love you better.[8]

Monopolies and licences had been given for the import, export and sale of such daily necessaries as currants, iron, powder, cards, horns, shin-bones, train-oil, clothes, ashes, bottles, bags, ain-seed (aniseed), vinegar, sea-coals, steel, aqua vitae, rushes, pots, salt, saltpetre, lead, oil, transportation of leather, dried pilcer, and almost any other commodity or service for which a courtier close to the crown or a friend, or a member of the Privy Council saw a profit and chose to ask.[9]

The existence and granting of these monopolies stirred general indignation. Petitions were presented to the Queen in her walks abroad. Cries were heard, 'God prefer those that further the overthrow of these monopolies . . . God send the Prerogative to act not our liking'.

The Queen at this time was getting old and she did not consider the times propitious to defend her right of royal prerogative. She yielded to the complaints and issued a proclamation declaring 'all patents null and void'. Eighty members of Parliament went up to her later thanking her for the proclamation,[10] such was their loyalty to her 'Princely Dignity'.

When James I came to the throne he was not restrained by Elizabeth's declaring 'all patents null and void'. While reigning in Scotland he had always been short of ready money for his personal living expenses. Now, lured by promises that he would have 'full purse' without having to go to Parliament, he yielded to the pressures of his favourites

---

[8] R. H. Tawney and E. Power: *Tudor Economic Documents* (1924).
[9] W. H. Price: *The English Patents of Monopoly* (1906).
[10] Craik and Macfarlane: op. cit.

and courtiers, and granted monopolies almost indiscriminately, creating even more than ever had existed under Elizabeth. Later with the passage of time public clamour and indignation increased, and in 1609 James followed the example of Elizabeth and proclaimed a general revocation of all patents and monopolies.[11]

Finally, still under James I, Parliament passed the 'Monopolies Act' of 1624:

> All monopolies and all grants to any persons . . . for the sale, buying, selling, making, or using of anything within the realm . . . *except in the case of new inventions* . . . to be altogether contrary to the law of the realm, and so . . . to be utterly void and of no effect, and in no wise to be put in execution.[12]

So far in these pages the Crown has been encountered as lawmaker and economist, politician and statesman. But what sort of a person was this Queen Elizabeth that William Lee sought to approach for his patent? Reasonably may he have hoped that of all people a woman would appreciate his invention.

Linked with the Queen's taste for pleasure and her concern for 'My People', however, was her fluctuating parsimony.[13] Because of the low state of the royal finances, for instance, due to the necessary measures for national defence and to the political and financial aid she had extended to the United Provinces and the French Huguenots, she compelled Lord Burghley to adhere to a rigid superintendence of all details of the public economy. To his credit was his judicious handling of the bill in the ensuing Parliament respecting the patrimonial estates of the collectors of taxes and duties who were liable for their arrears to the Queen; when the Commons desired that the arrears should not be made retroactive, Burghley retorted: 'My Lord, if you had lost your purse, would you look back or forwards to find it?'

[11] Craik and Macfarlane: op. cit.   [12] 21 James I. Cap 22.
[13] Lucy Aikin: *Memoirs of the Court of Elizabeth* (1818).

This kind of rigid parsimony endeared Elizabeth to the people, and they were safeguarded by it from the imposition of new and oppressive taxes. The traits of the Queen's complex character ranged from the protection of the people's purse to her personal pleasure. But her own self-love and acquisitiveness betrayed her extraordinary taste for personal magnificence, to the extent that her nobles found themselves actually economically burdened by the long visits she paid them attended by her enormous retinue at their country estates, as well as by contributions to her jewellery and wardrobe under the name of New Year gifts.

In the lists of the latter were 'not only rich jewels and rich robes but, significantly for the Maiden-Queen, every ornamental article of dress; sets of body-linen worked with black silk around the bosom and sleeves were regarded as no inappropriate offering from the Peers of the Realm'.[14]

Of another sort but also intended to bring them favour from her hands were the presents from Bishops and some of the nobility, consisting of gold pieces to the value of from £5 to £30.[15] Even this welcome gift was fittingly bestowed in silk purses, a far cry from William Lee's simple offering of loom-knit woollen stockings.

Fickleness was shown in her selective reciprocity in gifts of gilt plate, not always bestowed upon the same persons from whom she received presents, nor to an equal amount. Conspicuously absent among the crowd of admirers with whom she liked constantly to surround herself were the 'inferior' suitors and court attendants; these she 'seduced not by royal favours and gifts but by hollow smiles and flattering speeches, condemning them to long years of irksome, servile and sometimes profitless assiduity'.

Edmund Spenser, author of the *Faerie Queen*, expressed 'the injuries he had to endure, from the bitterness of his soul, of his profitless court attendance' and of the unfortunate sufferings of other courtiers:

[14] Aikin: op. cit.
[15] Conyers Read: *Mr Secretary Cecil and Queen Elizabeth* (1955).

Full little knowest Thou, that hast not tried,
What Hell it is, in suing long to bide . . .

To fawn, to crouch, to wait, to ride, to run,
To spend, to give, to want, to be undone.[16]

The person who made it possible for William Lee to gain access to the Court was Richard Parkyns, one of the two members of Parliament from Nottinghamshire, who was also a Barrister of the Inner Temple and County Recorder and Keeper of the Rolls. He arranged for Lee to meet Henry Carey, Lord Hunsdon, who at that time was also a member of the Queen's Privy Council and Lord Chamberlain of the Queen's household.[17]

Henry Carey was born in 1525, the only son of the William Carey who married Mary Boleyn, a sister of Anne Boleyn who was the mother of Queen Elizabeth. Lord Hunsdon, therefore, was a first cousin of the Queen. Appropriate too was the fact that William Carey, his paternal grandfather and the founder of the family fortune, had been a leading member of the Mercers Guild and a successful merchant in London.[18]

This was the same Lord Hunsdon who in 1572, according to the Records of the Borough of Nottingham, was given 'on the 24th day of August, two gallons of wine and one pound of sugar'.[19] 'Sack and sugar whenever he passes through . . . or pays an official visit to musters, or settles a dispute . . . constant favours to keep his pleasure, was the reward of the influential Lord'.[20] At the time of this record he was Governor of Berwick.

According to the practice prevailing in Elizabethan England of granting patents and monopolies, Lord Hunsdon was the perfect sponsor to help Lee to secure the desired patent.

[16] Edmund Spenser: *Mother Hubbard's Tale* (1603).
[17] J. Orange: *History of Nottinghamshire* (1840).
[18] *Dictionary of National Biography.*
[19] Records of the Borough of Nottingham.
[20] A. L. Rowse: *The Expansion of Elizabethan England* (1955).

At Elizabeth's Court the device of sponsorship on someone's behalf could be no more effective than was the degree of the Queen's favouritism extended to the sponsor. To determine the nature of the Queen's acceptance of Lee's genius, it is necessary first to assess her responsiveness to Hunsdon, her cousin. Several episodes are recorded concerning Hunsdon's relationship with her Majesty, revealing a certain obsequiousness on the part of the courtier and ungraciousness on the part of the Royal patroness. Unfortunately Hunsdon did not follow the practice, once described by her favoured god-child, John Harrington:

> Trust not a friend to do or say
> In that yourself can sue or pray.

Each time that Hunsdon sought something for himself when in the line of duty, he chose the Earl of Leicester for his liaison. Leicester was, 'confessedly, one of the deepest dissemblers of the age'.[21] Added to the fact that the flattering Leicester was avaricious in his play for the solid tokens of Royal favour, dependent on the capricious nod and coquetry of the Queen, the Hunsdon-Leicester-Queen line of access became a blind alley that only further hindered the inventor Lee in seeking to bring himself to the Queen.

Why exactly was Hunsdon not an 'insider' within the Elizabethan Court? Certainly he deserved much at her hands, for he had expended several thousand pounds of his own patrimony in her service during the time of her imprisonment.[22] Though she conferred on him the title of Baron and gave him the royal residence of Hunsdon, his remuneration was relatively small.[23] Perhaps the answer can be found in Hunsdon's character which differed from the Queen's. He was simple, direct, and honest. Too little skilled was Lee's sponsor in the 'ceremonious and sentimental gallantry which the Queen required from her courtiers, as in the circumspect and winding policy she approved in her statesmen'.

[21] Aikin: op. cit. [22] Froude: *History of England* (1867).
[23] Conyers Read: op. cit.

When the Queen appointed Hunsdon, her generous kins-man, as Governor of Berwick, she seemed to consult her own advantage and her country's by availing herself of the abilities of a diligent servant. Later he complained to Leicester about the unfavourable climate there, 'that it gave him the stone', using Leicester as the intermediary to win the Queen's permission for a holiday from his post. But the Queen's favourite did not succeed in Hunsdon's behalf.[24]

In 1589 following her policy of judiciously allotting key-posts to her closest relatives so as to gain from their con-scientiousness and vigilance, Elizabeth made Hunsdon Lord Warden of the Whole Marches. Repressed memories of her beheaded mother seemed to be in the picture of her association with her mother's relatives, reflected in the nature of this difficult assignment of the postern gate of her king-dom to Hunsdon, which he served for thirty years, and about which he complained that she kept him too short of money, 'that he was fed on pap, from the yolk of an owl's egg'.[25]

Growing older and tormented by gout, he finally looked for relief from the climate of the North and again appealed to Leicester to plead with the Queen to get him leave to come South. He hoped, 'Her Majestie will give me leave to seek some remedy for this Hellish disease . . . which, if it breed awhile will be incurable'.

With or without leave, he overstayed himself in the South. This time Elizabeth spared Leicester the task of purveying bad tidings and in great rage called to Hunsdon's son, Robert, to tell his parent 'that she would set you by the feet . . . if you dallied thus'. Lord Hunsdon returned North at once.[26]

Though Hunsdon lived in a ruffling time and loved sword and buckler men, his essential make-up was one of tender-ness. He was the only one of the Queen's Councillors to

[24] A. L. Rowse: *The England of Elizabeth* (1950).
[25] Ibid.
[26] Sir Robert Naunton: *Fragmenta Regalia. Observations on the late Queen Elizabeth, her Times and Favourites* (1653).

show any sympathy for the young James, King of Scotland, in his time of loneliness and poverty. The same traits of sympathy and friendliness Hunsdon brought to his association with William Lee. In his view the inventor merited royal acknowledgement.[27]

Hunsdon himself was not without business experience for he had exported woollen cloths to the Continent and the Low Countries, one year receiving a licence for the exportation of 20,000 cloths.[28] Because of his connections with the textile field he may have discerned, what Burghley may not have seen, the very real possibilities of Lee's loom and the great national economic advantages that could develop from it.

William Cecil, Lord Burghley, the Queen's Treasurer, was the one member of her Privy Council whom she considered 'exercised an incessant and watchful scrutiny over all aspects of the state's well-being'. While she associated with him, 'bearing in mind the well-being of the people', his economic conservatism had shown itself as early as 1559 when Elizabeth came to the throne:

> Those who depend on the making of cloth, are of worse condition to be quickly governed, than the husbandmen (farmers).[29]

Again in 1563 he added to his stated aim 'to remedy the shortage of agricultural labour' his advising reduction of entry into the occupation of merchant, which he termed a 'cloak for vagabonds and thieves'. He thought it an ill plan to encourage manufactures at the expense of tillage, for war might come at any time and throw the country back on its resources.

A statute that he favoured was the law designed to return to agriculture and tillage all lands which had been enclosed for sheep-grazing during the reign of Henry VIII. By the

---

[27] *Dictionary of National Biography.*
[28] *Calendar of State Papers. Domestic, Elizabeth* (1589). Vol. CCXXIX. No. 101.   [29] Conyers Read: op. cit.

12. Queen Elizabeth I (1533–1603), reigned 1558–1603. Artist unknown.

Clothworker   Tailor

Hatter   Dyer

13. Sixteenth-century woodcuts illustrating contemporary textile trades, by Jost Amman, Zürich.

same token he was in support of enactments that would return people to farm labours, in which group he placed the Statute of Artificers. Its provision that every craftsman in town or country should spend seven years as an apprentice to learn his craft tended to deter men from being clothiers, thus 'it would decrease the multitude now occupied therein, and would force some to employ themselves with cottage handicrafts and farm work'.[30]

To be confronted with any problem of local unemployment vexed Burghley to the extent that he maintained an extreme position: 'rather that there be grown by idleness any inconvenience, it were better to collect the sturdier and stronger sort of men, and send them to Ireland to help the peopling of the countries there'.[31] By 'better' he meant the avoiding of unemployment through promotion of agriculture and cottage industries.

The whole of Burghley's economic thinking was toward 'autarky', that is, towards economic self-sufficiency. The fundamental inconsistency of his position was that 'he wanted at the same time to increase British shipping with its market for raw materials, and to cut off the exchange of foreign luxury goods for British staples, which was the very core of overseas trade'.[32]

In 1572 the Spanish Minister, Mendoza, wrote to his King 'it is Burghley who rules the whole this country', and this trust of the Queen in her chief councillor extended throughout his public life. Even in 1598, De Maisse the French Ambassador was writing home, 'The Lord Treasurer is the principal man in her Council . . . The Queen trusts him in her most urgent affairs . . . It is he who can accomplish everything in England with the Queen.'

In his life of Lord Burghley Arthur Collins in 1732 described his influential role in these terms:

The Queen, never resolving any course of estate without his counsel, nor seldom passes any private suit for

---

[30] Froude: op. cit   [31] Ibid.   [32] Conyers Read: op. cit.

herself, that was not first referred to his consideration, and had his approbation before it passed.

Such were the imponderables far beyond the humble experiences of William Lee when he sought the influence of Lord Hunsdon, his highborn neighbour in Nottinghamshire, to approach the Queen on his behalf. He could not have known that the Queen's cousin was not completely in her favour or that he used Leicester as his go-between.

In any case hard behind the throne stood the all-powerful figure of Lord Burghley, more in favour of conservation then change.

The subject of the loom most certainly will have been discussed between the Queen and Burghley even before Lee 'performed and exercised' it in front of her though no documentary evidence that he influenced her decision survives.

EIGHT

'Performes his Loome before the Queene'

WILLIAM LEE eagerly waited for his sponsor, Lord Hunsdon, to interest the Queen in the invention. Lord Hunsdon planned to make arrangements for her Majesty to visit Lee's workroom to inspect the loom in actual operation. This he succeeded in doing and the inventor was about twenty-five years old and James, his younger brother only ten when the arrangements for the visit were completed.

The historian Thoroton simply records 'William Lee invented a loome to knit, in which he, or his brother James, performed and exercised before Queen Elizabeth'.[1]

The traditional story of the Queen's visit to Lee's workroom in Bunhill Fields is told by Henson:

'Having now discovered the method of knitting by machinery, his next effort was directed to obtain the golden harvest which had flattered his imagination. He removed his invention to London, for the purpose of presenting it before the Queen, in the fond hope of receiving her congratulations and those of the whole Court. Elizabeth was excited by curiosity. In company with Lord Hunsdon and his son, she went, incognito, to inspect the frame.'[2]

To the great advantage of Lee and his invention, clothes and fashion always fascinated the Queen, from her very earliest days when Lady Bryan beseeched the King's Chancellor for the motherless child 'that she may have some raiment', right to her later years when in 1600 an inventory showed more than 2000 pieces of feminine finery in her

[1] R. Thoroton: *Antiquities of Nottinghamshire* (1677).
[2] G. Henson: *History of Frame-Work Knitting and Lace Trades* (1831).

wardrobe.[3] Her reactions to Lee's machine and its products should be seen against the background of this absorbing interest in dress.

Of her qualities of mind her tutor, Roger Ascham, wrote in 1551 when she was eighteen years old, 'She excels in every kind of learning; the constitution of her mind, except from female weakness, is endowed with a masculine power of application'.[4] But in her aquiline nose and shape of her brow she resembled her father, Henry VIII, when he was young, eager, and handsome.[5]

After she had tasted the full power and prerogative of Queenship, another facet of her personality was manifest . . . exhibitionism. She demanded at all times that she be presented in character as Spencer's Gloriana . . . the 'greatest, glorious Queene of Faerie Lande'. If portraits were to be painted of her and shown to her beloved people, she would not allow what she considered uncomplimentary to be exhibited. There is a draft of a proclamation in Cecil's handwriting:

> Prohibiting all paynters, prynters and gravers, from drawing Queen Elizabeth's picture, until some conning person . . . mete therefore, shall make a natural representation of her Majestie's person, favour or grace, as a pattern for other persons to copy.[6]

But in 1560, with all her gorgeous clothes, toilettes, and hair-dressings, by contrast she found the stockings she wore ill-fitting. The cut and sewn hose were inelastic, not having the clinging qualities of the knitted stockings which would make her legs seem so elegant and the feel of the fabric so pleasant.

Sir Thomas Gresham, popularly called the 'Queen's Merchant and Banker', had a factor in Seville, Spain, who

[3] Henry Ellis: *Original Letters* (1842 edition).
[4] Roger Ascham: *Letters and Works* (1701).
[5] Elizabeth Jenkins: *Elizabeth the Great* (1959).
[6] *Calendar of State Papers. Domestic*, 1563. No. 25.

secured for him the hand-knit silk stockings which he gave
to royalty and were so highly prized.[7] Edward VI, whose
reign as King was cut short by early death, was a royal
recipient of hand-knitted silk stockings brought in by
Gresham from Spain: 'Edward VI had a paire of long
Spanish silke stockings, sent him for a great presente.'[7]
Stow adds that 'the gifte derived its value from the scarcity
of the object'.

Lord Burghley, Queen Elizabeth's principal Secretary,
accepted Sir Thomas's largesse, including gifts of silk
stockings. In 1560 Gresham wrote to Lord Burghley: 'I
have written into Spayne for silke hose . . . both for you,
and for My-Lady, your wife.'[8] A few days later in a letter
accompanying the gift he wrote: 'I have sent you herewith
two payre of black knit silke hoses . . . (undecipherable)
payre for My-Lady, your wife.'

While Lord Burghley willingly accepted the gift of this
super-luxury item, silk hand-knit stockings, from Sir
Thomas, he had strong beliefs concerning what he thought
was best for the economy of the country, especially what the
commonalty should wear. Under his sponsorship, Parliament
had passed a strict sumptuary law:

> That the common people should not wear expensive
> and rich dress to their impoverishment.
> Nor that any of the maid-servants, use or wear any
> hoses, when the payr shall exceed in price XIIId.[9]

Although Sir Thomas was a great favourite of the Queen,
there is no mention in the New Year 'Gifte list of the Queene'
for the year 1560 of a gift from him of silk-knit stockings;
it was the accepted custom that if one sought to retain a
favoured position in the Court, the surest was to give
the Queen an important New Year's gift and indeed silk-
knit stockings would have been in that category.

[7] John Stow: *The Annales or General Chronicles of England* (1615).
[8] T. W. Burgon: *Life and Times of Sir Thomas Gresham* (1839).
[9] 2 Eliz. C. 19.

However, Elizabeth was not deprived of 'silk hoses', for 1560 was the year when Mrs. Montague, her silk-woman, presented her Majesty with the famous pair of hand-knit ones of silk, for the traditional offering. The Queen responded: 'I like silke stockings so well . . . so pleasant, fine and delicate. Henceforth, I will wear no more cloathe stockings.'

John Alexander, a frame-work knitter, wrote about this episode in *Ye Historie of Ye First Paire of Silke Stockings, made in this country and worn by Elizabeth*:[10]

'On that New Year's Day, when Mrs. Montague presented the black silk stockings her girls had knitted, Lord Leicester and Lord Burghley were with the Queene, in her presence chamber. The Queene, examining closely the gossamer-like substance of the stockings, said: "They are so soft and beautiful."

'After a moment in deep admiration, she continued, "Methinks they are too frail to wear".

'Mrs. Montague, knowing well the strength of the hand-knit silk fabric, reassured her Majestie, "Though they look so frail, they are strong as cloathe hose".

'The Queene turned to Lord Leicester, and asked his opinion. Lord Leicester replied, "My Gracious Lady, they are fit for the fairies to wear, and as your Gracious Majestie is all beautiful, in fact a Fairie Queene, wanting but this gossamer-wear to perfect your attire".

'They say this Lord Leicester flattered much. And, as it amused the Queene, he did attain great position and many favours and monopolies.

'Lord Burghley's opinion was then asked. And as he was rather angry with Leicester's idea being taken in priority to his, and they each to the other have no great love, in fact, quite the opposite, he stated in his bluff way, "Good honest cloathe hose weare well enough for every one to use, and her Majestie wearing such things as silke hose, would upset

[10] John Alexander: Printer and frame-work knitter in Chancery Lane, London (1884).

the cloathe hose trade, that lead to new extravagances among the people".

'The Queene looked not pleased. The smile which had been about her face, at the idea of donning the new hose faded. Lord Burghley, bluff and rough, had struck a little home, for rather strict sumptuary laws had been passed by the Queene in which she laid down that the people should not weare over rich dress to their own impoverishment.

'The Minister Burghley saw he had made an impression, and had he stopped there, knitted stockings might not have come into vogue for another generation; and having made in his head a careful mathematical calculation, unfortunately for himself from wrong premises, for he had worked upon the thought that everybody stood on as solid a foundation as himself, gazed intently at the narrow, fragile things, and could not by any possibility grasp how any ordinary human being could by any possibility be gotten into them.

'He further, remembering the size of the clumsy cloathe hose, said to her Majestie: "Besides, these things could not by any possibility . . . fit . . . fit . . . fit." Here he stammered. He could say no more. He felt, to say the least, he was on delicate ground.

'Lord Leicester saw this opportunity, and bowing low, said: "Most Gracious Lady . . . design to try . . . try . . . try." And then, he too actually began to stammer.

'Good Queene Elizabeth looked upon the whole affair in a calm, quiet way and said, "Inasmuch as one noble gentleman saith the stockings could not fit, and the other suggested she should try . . . and see if they did fit . . . I would do so out of curiosity".

'Turning she told Mrs. Montague to follow to her sleeping-chamber, and directed Lord Burghley and Lord Leicester to wait her return.

' "Gentlemen", she said, after she had kept them waiting an hour, "The stockings do fit me right well, and I like them much, because they are pleasant, fine, and delicate. Henceforth I will weare no more cloathe stockings."

'Lord Leicester could not disguise the joy he felt at having overcome Lord Burghley. He cared nothing about the stockings, and said many flattering, nice things to her Majestie, which she was just in the humour of receiving.

'Lord Burghley stood by, frowning and looking angry. He had, he thought a logical reason being angry that the Queene took to her new stockings. The Queene then said: "Why do you not say merry things, my Lord Burghley, as does Lord Leicester?"

'After a moment's silence she added: "However, you Gallants shall be paid for waiting so long for me. This is the last pair of cloathe hose worn by me. I shall never wear the like again. I present them to you, my Lord Leicester, for after all, it was through you I tried the new hose, with which I am so pleased. And as for you, my Lord Burghley, ever thoughtful of how we can better serve our country and our people, I do not think this new fashion of mine will do hurt. It may bring up a new trade, in which many of my people will be employed. So, look no longer unhappy. I promise this first pair of knitted silk hose, which I now weare, shall be yours, to be kept by you in remembrance of this really interesting event."

'With this she dismissed them from her presence. Before doing so she said with true Queencraft: "The world need know little of my silk hose." '

The chronicler of the story recognized Elizabeth's traits of capriciousness and dalliance, which later Lord Hunsdon would need to try to surmount as sponsor in Lee's behalf. She would have liked that 'the world need know little' of the pleasure she experienced as she put on the hand-knit silk stockings, but at the same time she hoped that somehow the problem foreseen by Lord Burghley would not arise to harass her, and that there would still be equal opportunities for both the makers of cut and sewn stockings and for the hand-knitters of woollen and silk hose. She had not yet foreseen the third angle in the triangle: William Lee's loom-knit stockings.

While the Queen was donning the silk stockings, thoughts of the problems his government might face sobered Lord Burghley perhaps. Apprenticeship, the rise in prices, enclosures . . . these were only a few of the matters that had to be solved and would keep the Privy Council busy without end. If the wearing of silk hand-knit stockings came into vogue, the Merchant Taylors who made the cut and sewn stockings might suffer a loss of trade and consequent unemployment.

Lord Burghley was soon to assume the post of Lord Treasurer and the most important problems would come to him for ultimate consideration and advice to the Queen. As he was worrying about the new trade of silk hand-knit stockings, bringing new questions to the government, he may have remembered the Queen's charge to him, the day of his appointment as Principal Secretary:

> I give you this charge, that you take pains for me and my realm, and without thought to my private will, you will give me that counsel which you might think best.[11]

'Without thought to the Queen's private will' . . . was at that moment, with the donning of the silk stockings, raising a problem indeed, presenting him with many inner conflicts during his lifetime's service to his Queen.

Although Lord Burghley and Lord Leicester were practically sworn to secrecy by the Queen's 'The world need know little . . .', it was said that Lord Leicester, true to character, repeated the story to some of his friends, boasting how he had bested Lord Burghley.

In a wardrobe account of that period the entry appears: 'To Alice Montague, the Queen's Majestie's silke-woman, for sending her necessaries by her delivered, to her Majestie, . . . £702. 7s. 4d.'[12] In the same account of wardrobe expenditures, the annual salary of one Henry Henne, listed as the Queen's hosier, was given as £11. 7s. 10d. It would

[11] James A. Froude: *History of England* (1867).
[12] Herbert Norris: *Costume and Fashion* (1938).

seem that the entry for £702 paid for much more than silk
yarn for the Queen's stockings, including perhaps many ells
of flimsy silk chiffons and heavy brocades as well. According
to Nicholls there was a royal wardrobe 'for those that came
after' . . . since Elizabeth had made no will . . . 'a rich
wardrobe of 2000 gownes'.

According to tradition, it took Mrs. Montague and her
girls almost ten years to develop the 'arte and misterie' of
knitting silk stockings by hand, using as a model and pattern
the silk-knit hose which Sir Thomas Gresham presented to
Edward VI. The ambivalent wish of the Queen continued
in her demand for silk stockings and that 'this new fashion
of mine may bring up a new trade in which many of my
people may be employed'. For her, this notion transcended
Burghley's fears of the displacement of cut and sewn
stocking makers.

Queen Elizabeth's subjects recognized her interest and
concern in their skills in the handicrafts of spinning, weaving,
and knitting. The chronicler, Holinshed, described a pageant
incorporating these crafts presented during the Queen's
Progress to Norwich in 1578 and the 'receiving of the
Queen's Majestie into her City of Norwich':

'The first pageant was on Saint Stephen's Parish, in this
manner. It was builded like the manner of a stage, XL feet
longe, in breadth VIII foote. From the standing place up-
ward was a boothe, framed in the manner of a free stone-
wall, and in the height thereof was written these sentences:

> The causes of the Commonwealth are: God Truly
> Preached, The People Obedient, Labour Cherished,
> Justice Duly Exercised, Idleness Expelled, Universal
> Concord Preserved.

'From the standing place downward, it was beautiful with
painters' work, artificially exposing to the sight the portraiture of these several loombes, and the weavers in them, (as
if they were working) and over every loombe the name of
the work thereof.

'And then there was the portraiture of a matron, and two or three children, and over her head was written these words, "Good Nurture Changeth Qualities'.'

'Upon the stage there stood, at one ende, eight small women children, spinning worsted yarn, and at the other ende as many, knytting of worsted yarn hose. And in the midst of the sayd stage, there stood a prettie boy, richly apparelled, which represented the commonwealth of the citie, who said:

We bought before the things we now sell,
These slender imps their workes do pass the waves,
Gods peace on thine we hold and prosper well.
Of every mouth, the hands the charges save,
Thus, through Thy helpe and aid of power divine
Does Norwich live, whose hearts and goods are thine.

'This pleased her Majestie so greatly, as she particularly viewed the knittinge and spinninge of the children, perused the loombes, and noted the several workes and commodities which were made by their means. And then, after grate thanks by her given to the people, she marched toward the market-place.'

Indeed the Queen was grateful for the skills and commodities displayed in this exhibition of handicrafts. The sentiments expressed in the staged pageant, of 'Labour Cherished' and 'Idleness Expelled', confirmed her policy to 'sette the poore to worke'. Truly she might have hoped this would make for 'Universal Concord Preserved' as the aphorism, blazoned on the booth, proclaimed.

The people of Norwich, too, were proud no doubt of the 'prettie boy and eight small women-children, spinning worsted yarns and knitting worsted yarne hose'. The use of child-labour was an accepted feature of the economy in the Tudor period, even though young children worked for twelve to fourteen hours a day.

Philip Stubbes, often called 'that perennial voicer of complaints', criticized the fashion of hand-knit silk stockings, the demand for which had grown enormously by the time he wrote his book in 1583:[13]

'. . . then have they nether-stocks in these gay hosen (not of cloth, though ever so fine, for that is thought too base, but of jarnsey, worsted, silk thread and the like) so curiously knit with open seam down the leg, with quirks and clocks above the ankles, and sometimes haply interlaced with gold or silver thread, as is beautiful to behold.

'And so much insolency and outrage is not given, everyone, (almost) though otherwise verie poor, having scarce fortie shillings of wages by the yeare, will be sure to have two or three paire of these silk nether-stocks, or else of the finest yarn that may be got.

'Though the price of these be a Royal, or twentie shillings, as commonly it is! For how can they be less, when the very knitting is worth a noble, or a royal, or much more. The time hath been when one might have clothed his body well, from top to toe, for less than a paire of these nether-stocks will cost . . .'

At Hatfield House, once the property of Lord Burghley, there is a pair of hand-knitted silk stockings, said to have been worn by Queen Elizabeth.[14] Knit from a silk thread almost as coarse as string, the 'gossamer-like substance' of her day . . . 'over the whole surface of the stocking, dyed a deep sulphur yellow, are embroidered lozenges'.[15] Little did the Queen realize that her wish—'the world need know little of my silk stockings'—would fail of fulfilment. Lee himself could have known little of these affairs as he 'performed and exercised' before the Queen at Bunhill Fields. Unfortunately the Queen was not impressed. Henson describes the scene in this way:[16]

'Lee now imagined himself certain of a handsome remuneration, but his hopes proved delusive. It is said

---

13 Philip Stubbes: *The Anatomie of Abuses* (1583).
14 Norris: op. cit.
15 Lozenges = Small diamond-shaped figures.
16 Henson: op. cit.

nothing could exceed her disappointment, when she perceived that Mr. Lee was not making silk, but woollen stockings, and his machine was not capable of making the article in which she took so much pride of being the first wearer.[17]

'Though supported by the powerful intercession of Lord Hunsdon, and his son Sir William Carey, a favourite with Elizabeth, the Queen refused either to make a grant of money, or grant Lee a monopoly or patent. Her answer is said to have been in the following import:

> My Lord. I have too much love for my poor peoples, who obtain their bread by the employment of knitting to give my money to forward an invention which will tend to their ruin, by depriving them of employment, and thus make them beggars.

> Had Mr. Lee made a machine that would have made silk stockings, I should, I think have been somewhat justified in granting him a patent for that monopoly, which would have affected only a small number of my subjects. But to enjoy the exclusive privilege of making stockings for the whole of my subjects, is too important . . . to grant any individual.

'Hopes were thus held out to this extraordinary man, that if he should make silk stockings, he might have hopes of a remuneration by a monopoly. He had the mortification to feel what so often had been experienced by his successors, that because he had not accomplished everything, he had done nothing.'

The Queen's reactions as a woman are understandable. In 1560 when Elizabeth was presented with the pair of silk stockings by Mrs. Montague, she said: 'I like them . . . so

[17] The first machine, having only eight needles to an inch, would have been too coarse to make silk stockings. The hose would have been extremely coarse, and contained an enormous quantity of silk. Each pair would have weighed at least one pound. (Henson.)

pleasant, fine and delicate . . .' The quality of the work made on Lee's frame-work knitting machine was inferior to that made by hand by her silk-women. Perhaps the coarse woollen stockings he knit for her on his loom reminded her too much of the coarse cut and sewn stockings to which she had developed an antipathy.

The Queen's flare-ups and flashes of temper indicated a character that could turn away in resentment on the slightest provocation. When she was handed Lee's pair of coarse woollen stockings, she may have had a feeling of revulsion against the stockings and transferred that feeling to the unfortunate maker of the machine himself. Only silk stockings befitted her royal dignity and position; she, the Queen no longer wore coarse woollen stockings. She had anticipated receiving fine silk stockings and her reaction was abrupt. The stockings were an insult; her vanity had been seared.

So perhaps it was expedient for the Queen to accept Burghley's unfavourable reaction, when he argued the probability of technological displacement of the hordes of hand-knitters taught in the knitting schools set up by the local authorities 'to sette the poore to worke'. His opinion will have included more than the simple market facts relating to the price of hand-knit stockings, which were relatively recently introduced in England and high in price, with hand-knit worsteds being sold as high as 9 shillings a pair. Loom-knitting would not at that time have been considered a *new* industry but as a modification of the then existing hand-knitting craft, the latter not very old and pre-existing.[18]

The spectre of unemployment of those engaged in the trade of hand-knitting may well have appeared to Elizabeth as a genuinely distasteful, perpetual menace. She had the experience of the 'decay' of the hand-knitting of woollen caps, followed by the influx of aliens who became hand-knitters of woollen and worsted stockings with consequent effect upon the makers of cut and sewn stockings. Now the hand-knitters of stockings might be displaced by the loom-

[18] F. A. Welles: *The British Hosiery Trade* (1935).

knitters introduced by Lee, the 'frame-work' knitters as they would be called.

Other trades besides the knitting crafts threatened unemployment. In 1591, a petition came to the Queen on behalf of the 'handicraftsmen of the Misterie of Skinners':

> Vouchsafe, dear Sovereign, of your most gracious compassion, to your grateful subjects, the poor, miserable, decayed people, handicraftsmen of the Misterie of Skinners, of London. When their predecessors were not only of competency to live, but also to supply subsidies, loans and like services, now decayed, by that the usual wearing of furs is utterly neglected, and eaten out by the too ordinary lavish and unnecessary use of velvets and silkes.[19]

Lee's plea for royal aid came at a time, too, when the Royal Treasury was in such poor condition that the Queen sought new sources of revenue rather than new enterprises for investment. She was more interested in privateering ventures in which she risked little or no capital, and was rewarded with flat percentages of all prize ships and booty taken, than in aiding inventions with problems in their wake.

In the years 1589–1593 she spent at least £300,000 in the aid of Henry IV of France. Apart from the Irish Wars and naval expenditures in that same period her total spending was over £800,000.[20] In one year she was under the necessity of selling Crown Lands to the value of £120,000. In 1588 she made use of a loan from the City. In August of that year, and chiefly from the members of the 12 Great Livery Companies, the sum of £51,000 was raised, and again in 1589 another loan of £15,000 was made.[21]

Lord Hunsdon, however, was less cast down than William Lee by such considerations or by the Queen's lack of favour. If silk stockings were wanted instead of coarse woollen ones,

[19] Historical Mss. Commission. Part IV. *Hatfield*.
[20] J. E. Neale: *Elizabeth I and her Parliaments* (1953).
[21] Stow: op. cit.

he was confident that Lee would improve the machine and make them.

Henson writes: 'Lord Hunsdon, as well as his son Sir William Carey, was equally sanguine as to the making of silk stockings and obtaining the patent which they hoped to enjoy cojointly, and they determined to persevere . . . As a preliminary it was agreed that Mr. Lee should teach Sir William (afterwards the second Lord Hunsdon) the arte and misterie, and upon his requiring a guarantee for the security of the invention, Sir William offered to become his apprentice, which was accepted . . . Thus, the first stocking-maker's apprentice was a Knight, the eldest son of a Lord, who was of the blood royal.'[22]

According to a French writer, the fact that the inventor's association was with a Knight did not prevent the journeyman workers of stockings, together with the hand-knitters and cut and sewn makers, from venting their fears of unemployment and economic displacement in the only manner they thought possible. One day, the story runs, these workers not only attacked the noble apprentice, who was compelled to flee for safety, but also destroyed the machine they feared.[23]

Association of the Hunsdon family with William Lee, the famous inventor, brought forth a poetic broadside (author unknown) embellished by the coat of arms of the Frame-Work Knitters Guild.[24] Dedication was made To the

[22] Henson: op. cit.
[23] Georges Théry: *Recueil des Actes de la Vénérable Marie Poussepin*, Tours (1938).
[24] Later descendants of Lord Carey were also associated with the Guild. In an 'N.B.' on the bottom of a broadside, printed by a member of the Frame-Work Knitters Guild one, J. Davis, sometime in the early eighteenth century noted: 'Lord Carey, Earl of Hunsdon was admitted a member of this company, on the 25th of June, 1666, and in 1667, was admitted a workhouse keeper, and bound William Pope, apprentice . . .' At the time of Lord Carey, no frame-work knitter was permitted to take an apprentice, without giving a specimen of his knitting, and was afterwards called a 'Work-house Keeper'. A copy of this broadside is in the records of the Frame-Work Knitters Guild of London, in the Guildhall, London.

Memory of 'Great Genius, William Lee, Master of Arts of St. John's College, Cambridge, who devised this profitable art of making stockings . . .' Ironically, after the passage of time, Queen Elizabeth is highly praised:

> *In ancient days, when Dame Eliza reigned,*
> *and proved to infant arts a nursing friend,*
> *And made, by kind encouragement she gave*
> *To Scolar studious, and the soldier brave;*
> *Then every genius did his pow'r exert,*
> *And labour'd to advance some useful art.*

On the inventor's days in Cambridge the poet writes:

> *Among the rest, Lee of immortal fame,*
> *to learning bred upon the banks of Cam,*
> *To Great Bellona favour'd and inspir'd,*
> *raised a new engine (even now admir'd).*

On his romance with a maid and her knitting come these words:

> *Whose curious form in every art displays*
> *the force of love in those reforming days;*
> *for love, engaged by cruel neglect and spite*
> *First brought this artful stocking frame to light.*
> *That pretty maids, when woo'd might lay aside*
> *Their knitting, (which was their only pride)*
> *And be the more at leisure to attend*
> *The sighs and flatteries of an amorous friend.*

The anonymous poet then describes the machine, made of 'three thousand pieces':

> *Nor is there one device that can appear,*
> *more wondrous than the frame depicted here;*
> *Three thousand pieces doth the whole contain,*
> *The unwearied task one poor Scolar's brain:*
> *Who, in revenge of female slights was moved*
> *to spoil the knitting of the dame he loved.*

S.Q.—I

Since such a curious art that tends to gain,
Its origin we owe to proud disdain,
May each desponding lover pensive grow,
And when despised, the like resentment show!

The final lines contain a tribute to the Peer, Lord Robert Carey, Earl of Hunsdon, and the pride of the Guild in his membership:

Nor, is there one Mechanic Art, can name
A Peer, a workman . . . but the knitting frame;
who in his youth was to the engine bred,
And served seven years, Apprentice to the trade,
Wrought many years as modern fame records,
Yet lives to sit among his brethren Lords.
Since . . .
By a noble Peer, that work'd therein,
May the fam'd art be still more famous made,
And peaceful times with riches, bless the trade!

NINE

'Freedom of the Citie'

AFTER the Queen departed from the workshop in Bunhill Row, William Lee was in a state of depression. Having looked forward to her visit as a great honour, he perceived it had turned out a double disappointment: to his Queen because he could not knit on his machine the silk stockings she had expected to receive from him; to Lord Hunsdon because the Queen had rejected his sponsorship of Lee's invention.

As he sought to interpret the meaning of the Queen's words, the perseverance born of the influence of Perkins and Chaderton at Cambridge now stood him in good stead. While Elizabeth had said 'No', she had also said: 'I think I would have been somewhat justified in granting a patent . . . that would have affected only a small number of my subjects.'

Bringing his own resourceful mind to interpret the words of the Queen, he thought perhaps only a small number of a certain degree would wear silk-knit stockings and so . . . only a small number would be needed to knit them, thus affecting only a small number of handicraftsmen.

Henry VIII had issued a proclamation which Elizabeth had reaffirmed under her royal prerogative, that:

> . . . none under the degree of a Baron, or a Baron's son, or a gentleman attending her Majestic, shall wear netherstocks made of silk . . . nor shall any woman under the degree of a Baroness, or her daughters, wear sylke hose.[1]

Perhaps he also recollected another sumptuary law: '. . . the

[1] 'Proclamation, with certain clauses of Divers Statutes, first published, in the XIX yeare of the Queen's Majestie's reigne, and now reissued. John' Nichols: *Illustrations of the Manners and Expenses of Ancient Times in England* (1797).

silke stockings, being a foreign commodity, is prohibited, saving unto those of a certain degree'.[2] Believing that at all times his Queen, merciful and sincere, was 'thinking of my people', trusting and naive perhaps, he considered Elizabeth might use her royal prerogative to enforce the sumptuary law.

He made up his mind that all his energies must now be turned to perfecting the loom. No longer having the living of the Glebe House in Calverton, 'valued in the King's Book at 4£.', the task of supporting James and himself was a major problem. For the time being at any rate, financial aid from the Hunsdon family was uncertain. Even though Sir George Carey, Baron Hunsdon's oldest son, was engaged in privateering ventures in which the Queen and other members of the Court also shared, the privateering was extremely hazardous; the capital and profits of many voyages could be lost in one unfortunate encounter.

So William Lee decided to continue to knit wool stockings on the first loom, which he would try to sell, while endeavour to build a finer loom to make silk hose. The profits would enable them to live and purchase the materials necessary to build the new machine.

After many experiments he found that a satisfactory silk fabric would have to be knit $2\frac{1}{2}$ times finer than the fabric for a woollen stocking. The needle bar would have 60 needles to a 3 in. span, instead of 24.[3] Each of the 3000 pieces of the 'ingine' would be finer or stronger, proportionately, than in the first machine.[4]

Fortunately, not far from Bunhill Row, outside Bishopsgate in the Petty Fraunce area, there were excellent artisans, clockmakers and loom-smiths, refugees from Rouen. Weavers, skilled and expert in the handling of silk yarns which required different treatment from wool, were also available.

French merchants settled in London many years before

---

[2] *Calendar of State Papers. Domestic: Elizabeth*, Vol. CCXXXI Item 231.
[3] G. Henson: *History of Frame-work Knitting and Lace Trades* (1831).
[4] Frame-Work Knitters' Petition to Cromwell (1655–1657).

the Reformation, importing and exporting the wares of both countries. At a later date, following the first conflicts between Catholic and Huguenot, many refugees arrived. Some even became members of guilds, were granted letters of denization, and received the 'freedom of the city'.[5]

However, Lee realized that if he came into too open association with the 'straungers' he would arouse the antagonism of the native weavers and tailors. So, fearing he would be 'despised', as in Calverton, he held his meetings with them surreptitiously.

In a petition to Parliament the members of the guilds had claimed: 'The foreigner hawked his goods in the city, did not pay his charges, while the Englishman pays all his duties belonging to a subject, being himself, and all that he hath, ready to do the Queen and the city, service.'[6]

As early as May 1562, with the arrival of 500 destitute French at Dover, the Mayor there wrote at various times to Sir William Cecil: '. . . and we be in great want of corn for their and our sustenation . . . also may it please your honour, after nite and this day, is come 2 shippes of Dieppe, into this haven, full of many people.' On November 15, 1562, he wrote: 'there arrived a boat from Dieppe, with hundred and fiftye French, men, women and children'; on December 10, 1562, '. . . another bote, many poor people of Rouen'. In 1572, after the St. Bartholomew Day Massacre, the number increased to 644 adults: '. . . of gentlemen, merchants, doctors, ministers, shipwrights, labourers, who were in distress.'[7]

Though broadsides were printed that 'the natives became unquiet . . . that the strangers in all England were offensive to the ordinary sort of people', the protests did not prevent the influx of fugitive Frenchmen and denizens. In 1593 a bill was introduced in Parliament, alleging 'that the retailing of

---

[5] *Huguenot Society Publications.*

[6] C. M. Clode: *Memorials of the Merchant Taylors* (1875).

[7] Samuel Smiles: *The Huguenots, their Settlements, Churches, and Industry in England* (1868).

foreign commodities by strangers caused the decay of English retailers'. This brought from the refugees a defensive answer: '. . . the act would debar us from our living, that we sold wares better cheap than the English retailers, and the act was against our freedom of denization.' The bill was not passed and the door was left open to those who had fled from their homeland in religion's name.

Lee knew that in past years, especially in the fast-growing city of London, citizens had feared foreign craftsmen and mechanics, jealous of their bringing new skills to some already overcrowded trades like the cordwainers, fearful of having their jobs taken away. He was able to bide his time, finally enlisting the aid of the Rouenaisse skilled artisans and mechanics to help him construct the finer machine necessary to knit silk stockings.

Neither William Lee nor any gild-merchant, master or journeyman was a member of a free society with the right to develop in his craft or trade as fast as his imagination and ability allowed. Sumptuary laws, even without the authority of Parliament, ordered daily life in England from drink to dress. The apprenticeship statute of 1563, as well as the regulations of the individual guild controlling the weavers, the tailors, the haberdashers and the drapers, laid down the kind of stockings he could make, and their colour, price, style, and quality; how many apprentices he could employ, how long they should be employed, and what they must be paid.

Before Lee could think of setting up his shop in Bunhill Row, before he could hawk his stockings, the first requirement of the Court of Aldermen and of the guilds was that he possess the privilege of 'Freedom of the Citie'. Until he possessed this 'freedom' he would violate the 'customs of London'. Yet he could not acquire the privilege unless he were first a member of the guild which claimed jurisdiction over his special craft.[8]

[8] Rev. A. H. Johnson: *History of the Worshipful Company of Drapers of London* (1914).

This was not his only problem. Membership in a guild would not be granted unless he first served a seven-year apprenticeship under a guild-master. Lee could never hope to serve such an apprenticeship, even if he were willing, since there was no Master who had a loom or had knowledge of the mystery of frame-work knitting.

Here was the essential difference in the position of the inventor, William Lee, compared with the ordinary 'foreign brother' of 'straunger' who came to practice his craft within the liberties of London. Stockings 'knit on a steele engine' differed from cut-and-sewn or hand-knit stockings. It was a new trade, for 'the trade of frame-work knitting was never known or practised before it was invented by William Lee'.[9] Lee claimed that none of the established guilds had jurisdiction over his 'misterie'. It was as if loom-knit stockings had no paternity.

Because Lee could knit a pair of stockings on his loom many times faster than the hand-knitter, the haberdashers' guild was bound to oppose him and his new misterie in order to protect its members who were hand-knitters. London, Chester, and Bristol guilds had already 'refused the freedom of the city, upon a straunger, without the consent of the craftsmen of the occupation'.[10] Labour-saving devices were discouraged by the guilds; the 'putting-down' of gig-mills, and cloth-workers' opposition to new methods in the fulling of broadcloth, are but two examples. Within the guild philosophy of the times Lee was bound to meet refusal of guild membership.

The privilege of freedom of the city had its origin in medieval times. There were three methods whereby William Lee could acquire it.[11] First if he had been born in London he would have it as a natural right. The applicant had to be 'a man, born in the city, lawfully from his father'. Illegitimate children did not possess by patrimony the right of freedom

[9] Frame-Work Knitters' Petition to Cromwell.
[10] E. Lipson: *Economic History of England*, Vol. I, 12th Edition (1959).
[11] J. F. V. Woodman: *Freedom of the City* (1960).

of the city. There was also sex discrimination for it was specifically stated 'that he be a man'.

The second way whereby Lee could have secured the freedom would have been if he had served the seven years of apprenticeship with a freeman, which was the minimal requirement of the Statute of Artificers.

The last method open and the one adopted by Lee was called 'redemption', which was in fact securing 'freedom by purchase'. The applicant petitioned the Court of Aldermen and, 'compounding' with the chamberlain, he paid a specified, predetermined amount. Lee would find that the policy of the livery companies in granting freedom by redemption had varied over the centuries. When the demand for goods was poor and trade slow, requests for freedom by redemption were unwelcome and fees raised almost prohibitively. When trade was good and the demand for wares brisk, the fees were lowered. There was no standardization of the amount to be paid.

Another regulation that hindered Lee in the sale of his stockings was that 'no man, which as a furraine, shall buy or sell, within the liberties of the citie, with another furraine'. The purpose was to control all trade, both domestic and export. Since Lee in dire necessity no doubt sold some of his stockings to the 'straungers' for export, this particular regulation must have made life hazardous.

Despite the long years of conflict marked by impasse in his attempts to come under the appropriate guild control, or opposition on the part of the guild-members to accept the loom with its labour-saving potential, the Gordian knot was finally cut and Lee was admitted to the Weavers Guild as a foreign brother on March 7, 1608.[12]

With his admission to the Weavers Company, William Lee brought to an end his differences with the guilds. But there were new responsibilities; the guilds required their members to pay city and state tax assessments for specific

[12] Freedom Admission Books. The Weavers Company. Guildhall, London Folio 48. Vol. I, 1604-46. March 7, 1608.

purposes such as hospitals, supplies for the war, corn, subscriptions for loans to the Crown and participation in civic pageantries and ceremonies.[13] He also had to pay for his admittance as a foreign brother in the Weavers Company.

In their Freedom Admission Books, it is recorded:

> William Lee, weaver of silk stockings by an ingin, was on the 7th day of March, 1608, admitted a foreign brother, for three pounds, whereby he paid 20 shillings in hand.

> And the rest he is to pay, whereof he shall set up any loom, or 'sapyn', to use the art of weaving.[14]

Throughout the struggles of his London years Lee was always short of money. Although the total fee for admission to the Weavers Company was £3, it had been willing to accept payment for membership on two different dates. On an earlier date, possibly as a down payment, in Folio 47 an entry was made: 'William Lee, Received of him, when he was admitted, the sum of two pounds'.

On the later date of March 7, 1608, he completed the payment for there was the entry in Folio 48, 'whereof he paid 20 shillings in hand', making the completion of the full payment of £3, the sum he was 'sworn' to pay. So William Lee at long last attended both membership as a foreign brother and the required full payment of the membership fee of £3.

Now he was properly qualified to obtain freedom of the city. Here, although his petition was made on October 1, 1605, and antedated by almost three years his admission to the Weavers Guild, the Court of Aldermen would not have granted him the freedom until he fulfilled the primary requisite of guild membership. In the Proceedings of the Court, the entry reads:

> Item: The Petition of William Lee, Master of Arts, first inventor of an ingine to make silke stockings,

---

[13] Johnson: op. cit.   [14] Sapyn = Pine tree.

made to this Court, for his freedom of the city by redemption.

An for certain rooms, to be granted unto him, in Bridewell to work in.

By this Court referred to the consideration of Sir Stephen Soames, Sir John Garrard, Sir Thomas Bennett, Sir Humphrey Welles, and Sir Thomas Romeny, Knights.

Or to any three or more of them, as they to make report of this Court, or their opinions touching the same.[15]

Implicit obedience to the customs of the city and guild regulations was required of all having the freedom. It would have been necessary for Lee to have taken the Weavers' oath before the Chamberlain in the Chambers of the Court of Aldermen. His oath would have included an affirmative answer to:

Ye shall be goode and true to our Sovereign Lord, the King, and be obedient to the Mayor of the City, and maintain the customs and freedom of the City. Ye shall be a partner to all charges, and not avow the goods of foreigners as for yours, whereby the King shall lose his custom.

Ye shall take no apprentice for less than seven years, and if he be not free, and not bond.

And if ye know of any foreign merchandise, in the city, ye shall warn the Chamberlain.[16]

Before his admission to the Weavers Guild in 1608, William Lee in keeping with the trend in England toward

---

[15] Proceedings of the Court of Aldermen. City of London, October 1, 1605. Repertory 27. Folio No. 87.
[16] Arnold's Chronicles: *Customs of London* (1811).

individualism continued working, with mixed feelings no doubt, in his 'misterie' in spite of guild requirements. He was not alone in this respect for there are numerous records of the guild courts charging members with failure to obey the customs and regulations of the guilds of the City of London.[17] The rapid rise of rich merchants to positions of power made for an unwillingness to accept the intervention of the Crown in the functioning of the guilds. Many of the industrial regulations which the Privy Council asked the Magistrates to enforce were not embodied in the Statutes of the Realm but were based on Royal proclamations. Even the apprentice-ship records were not always kept in a systematic manner to ensure full enforcement.[18]

In Lee's Petition to the Court of Aldermen for freedom of the city, an additional request was included not common in many applications, indicating how difficult were Lee's early struggles for recognition. Lee petitioned for 'certain rooms, to be granted unto him, in Bridewell . . . to work in'. It was a sign of his determination to take advantage of any type of government aid while he continued in his efforts to improve his 'ingine to make silk stockings'.

There is no official record that he was either granted or denied the rooms. It can be assumed that the request was ultimately granted for, by fulfilling all the requirements of guild membership and receiving freedom of the city, 'though poor, he was a man of respectable character, honest life and upright dealing'.

Bridewell was a name for both opprobrium and succour. In 1570 John Stow wrote: 'the use of this hospital, Bridewell, now is for an house of correction, and to be a place for all strumpets, night-walkers, vagrants and idle persons, that are taken up for their ill-lives, as also incorrigible and disobedient servants are committed . . . And being so committed are forced to beat hemp in public view, with a correction of

---

[17] G. Unwin: *Industrial Organization in the 15th and 16th centuries* (1904).
[18] John U. Nef: *Industry and Government in France and England (1540–1640)* (1940).

whipping, according to their offence.'[19] Bridewell had another aspect and purpose, too, that of a trade-training school for the orphan and poor.

While Lee will have had the benefit of free apprentices, rooms, raw materials, and board, as well as of unskilled labour, there was also the disadvantage of having to work with sick, the indigent, the vagabond, and the prostitute. He was faced with the prospect of living and working in a sordid environment. Raised in pleasant Calverton, graduated from Cambridge, favoured by the Queen's consideration of his invention, he would of necessity now be compelled to work with an 'evil crew' of Bridewell inmates, teaching them the misterie of frame-work knitting . . . in return for bed and board.

Lee may have looked upon his petition for rooms in Bridewell as one step in his search for government subsidy, as a substitute for the aid he had been refused by the Queen. Moreover he may have accepted Bridewell, in the English system of poor relief, as identified with a sound purpose, for the training of orphans and homeless as apprentices in as many as twenty-six trades, met obligations of society.[20]

For the former curate, imbued with compassion for the woes of the indigent and handicapped, there was a challenge to teach and rehabilitate; he might succeed in training some state-supported apprentices in the 'misterie' of loom-knitting. But how could he train successfully the type of inmate assigned to him? They were the 'weaker sort of people, some lame . . . whose hands were to be occupied in carding, drawing of wire, knitting and winding of silk . . .' He would have certainty of meeting one regulation 'they shall be kept with their dyet . . . only sufficient to keep them in health'.

The Governors were obliged 'to set up certain artes and workes . . .' People who were admitted to train the youths to fulfil the apprenticeship requirements were first called 'worke-masters' and 'task-masters'. After 1569 the name

[19] John Stow: *Survey of London* (1630).
[20] *Bridewell Hospital Extracts from Records and Court Books* (1798).

was changed to 'artes-masters', also referred to sometimes as 'decayed artes-masters'.

Although not recorded as of the sixteenth century, a 1793 resolution of the Bridewell Governors perhaps discloses the basic reason of Lee's petition for the rooms in Bridewell: 'When the Governors found a trade a losing one, they determined to leave it off . . . they agreed with the artes-masters on a trade of a different description . . . offered to lend them money for stock . . . so as to train apprentices in a new trade.' Lee may have judged that, since loom-knitting was a new misterie or trade, it would be of interest to the Governors of Bridewell. To the persevering, ambitious inventor, the thought perhaps extended beyond their lending him money 'to buy materials for stock' to his own greater goal of building looms.

Altogether it took Lee ten long years to perfect a machine to make silk stockings. The lack of a patent did not discourage him from continuing his experiments. With some financial help from the Hunsdon family he rebuilt and re-needled his loom into a 24-gauge frame, replacing the 12-gauge one he had operated before the Queen. So it is recorded:

> In the year 1599 was devised and perfected, the art of knitting or weaving silke stockings, by engines or steele loomes, by William Lee.[21]

But Lee was never given the opportunity to perform his improved loom before the Queen. His sponsor, Lord Hunsdon, died in 1596. In 1598 the Queen's advisor, Lord Burghley, died. Finally the grantor of royal favour, the Queen herself, died in 1603.

Nor did Elizabeth's successor, James I, ever grant the inventor his due.

---

[21] Stow: op. cit.

TEN

Mercantilism in Rouen

DURING Lee's London years, when he was struggling to establish himself and gain recognition, rays of light came in the unfailing confidence of his young brother James and in a relationship with the Rouennaise weavers and clock-makers in Petty Fraunce and Spitalfields who gave him their help in his constant experimentation with improved versions of his looms.

In particular he came closely in touch with a well-known French entrepreneur, Pierre de Caux, and his brother Salomon who were both destined to play a decisive role in the inventor's future career.

Some of the de Caux family, leading Huguenots of Rouen, took refuge in England in 1590. Salomon de Caux was an eminent engineer, architect, inventor, and author who during his time in England served as tutor to Henry, Prince of Wales, eldest son of King James I.

Lee's invention may have attracted Salomon to London's Petty Fraunce where he himself was well known to many of his compatriots from Rouen and Dieppe.[1] Evidence seems to suggest that Salomon was instrumental in effecting the meeting of William Lee with his brother Pierre, who was particularly active in the secret assemblies of the Huguenot sect in the Rouen area, entering and re-entering the haven, England, frequently.[2]

At that time in France every effort was being made to establish new industries. Thirty-eight years of Catholic-Huguenot conflicts, at a cost of a million men and many

[1] Christina Sandrina Maks: *Salomon de Caux, Le fameux Ingénieur, Architecte et Musicien* (1935).
[2] E. and E. Haag: *La France Protestante* T. III, 2nd edition (1877).

millions of livres of property, had caused the ruin of manufactures, and had threatened trade and commerce. Though
there was a picture of comparative peace at the end of the
sixteenth century, through a seeming settling of religious
differences following the Edict of Nantes of 1598, the
heritage of war's evils was marked in the industrial area.
Foreign manufactures had usurped the French market.
Standards of quality were low in French manufactures.
Many of the superior Huguenot workers escaped to take
refuge in Holland and England, helping to found new
industries there, which would compete with those in their
native land. One half of France's population was unemployed, and many reduced to beggary.[3]

In the reign of Henry IV of France, the need for industrial
reform stimulated the development of the mercantile state.
As mercantilism dealt with the economic functioning of the
national state, all phases of economic life were brought under
royal control. Established to direct the commercial activities
was the Conseil du Commerce and appointed by the King
in 1601 to head it was a certain Barthélémey Laffemas, the
Controlleur Générale du Commerce.

The name, Laffemas, was to become well known to
William Lee. Former *valet du chambre* to Henry of Navarre
and born in 1545 of a poor Huguenot family, he was a man
with no formal schooling. His extreme positions on mercantilist theories, born out of a 'child-like belief in the
omnipotence and omni-competence of the central government', had as their starting point the need to prevent the
export of bullion, a shortage of which it was claimed caused
poverty in France.

To achieve this goal of conserving precious money, there
were related practices: restriction of imports of manufactured
goods; banning of luxury goods of foreign make; prohibition
of the export of raw materials needed for manufactures in
France; import of raw materials restricted to those required
for French manufactures; development of French sericul-

[3] P. Boissonade: *Le Socialisme d'État (1453-1661)* Paris (1927).

ture, mines, agriculture, and seapower.[4] In pursuit of these aims the French mercantilist state mobilized national patriotism, and hence there followed close identification with the Crown engendering dislike of foreigners, ranging from an attitude of indifference to a bitter, burning hatred.

According to the plans of Laffemas, the first task of the Conseil du Commerce, which was brought into existence to restore trade, was a consideration of ways to extend France's manufactures. The King issued edicts on Laffemas's advice, granting privileges and money to aid entrepreneurs and offering royal patronage to inventors by grants of exclusive rights for their inventions.

Here was a point of vital interest to the inventor, William Lee, as it was explained to him by Salomon and Pierre de Caux. An item of the Conseil du Commerce, *Procés Verbeaux*, in 1604, was particularly relevant:

> The interest of the Conseil, is not only to propositions of inventors and industrialists, but to their taking initiative in establishing new industries ... to introduce the making of stockings of silk and of wool.[5]

This *Recueil* augured that opportunity would be knocking at the door of the inventor, particularly the one with knowledge to introduce the making of stockings *au métier*[6] into France.

It was to the body of Notables of Rouen that the deliberations of the Conseil du Commerce were presented in projects related precisely to native manufactures. In Rouen the Notables had certain very specific tasks: to check importations of foreign-made goods with consequent outgoing of French money in payment; cultivation of silkworms to produce Rouen's own silk; ordinances for the improvements of silk hand-knit stockings to counteract the source of supply

---

[4] C. Wolsey Cole: *French Mercantilist Doctrines before Colbert* (1931).
[5] Gustave Fagniez: *L'Économie Sociale de la France, sous Henri IV* Paris (1897).
[6] Au métier = by machine.

TO THE
WORSHIPFUL COMPANY
OF
FRAME - WORK - KNITTERS

SPEED STRENGTH AND TRUTH UNITED

In the Year 1589, the Ingenious WILLIAM LEE, Master of Arts, of St JOHN'S COLLEGE, CAMBRIDGE, devis'd this profitable Art of Knitting STOCKINGS: But his Invention being despis'd, he went to FRANCE, Yet of IRON to him-self, but to us and others of GOLD. In Memory of so great a GENIUS this is here depicted.

In antient days, when Dame ELIZA reign'd,
Who prov'd to Infant Arts a nursing Friend,
And made, by kind Encouragement she gave,
The Scolar studious, & the Soldier brave;
Then ev'ry Genius did his Pow'r exert,
And labour'd to advance some useful Art:
Amongst the rest, LEE, of immortal fame,
To learning bred upon the banks of CAM,
By great BELLONA favour'd & inspir'd,
Rais'd a new Engine (even now admir'd)
Whose curious form in ev'ry Part displays
The force of Love in those reforming days;
For Love, enrag'd by cool neglect & spite
First brought this artful Stocking Frame to light,
That pretty Maid, when wood might lay aside
Their KNITTING (which was then their only Pride)
And be the more at leisure to attend
The Sighs and flatt'ries of an am'rous Friend.

Nor is there one Device that can appear
More wondrous than the FRAME depicted here.

Three Thousand Pieces doth the whole contain,
Th'unwearyd Task of one poor Scolars Brain;
Who, in revenge of Female flights, was mov'd
To spoil the KNITTING of the Dame he lov'd.

Since such a curious Art that tends to gain,
Its Origin we owe to PROUD DISDAIN,
May each desponding Lover pensive grow,
And when despis'd, the like Resentment show!

Nor is there one MECHANIC Art can name
A PEER a Workman but the KNITTING FRAME;
Who in his Youth was to the Engine bred,
And serv'd seven Years, Apprentice to the trade,
Wrought many Years as modern Fame records,
Yet liv'd to sit among his Brethren LORDS.

Since thus this useful FRAME has honour'd been
By a late noble PEER, that work'd therein,
May the fam'd Art be still more famous made,
And peaceful times with riches bless the trade!

NB. Lord Rt CAREY Earl of HUNSDON was admitted a Member of this Company on the 25th of June, 1666, and in 1677 was admitted a *Workhouse Keeper and bound Wm Pope Apprentice.

GEORGE SIMMONS, Beadle.

* In the Time of Lord CAREY, no FRAME-WORKE KNITTER was permitted to take an Apprentice, without first giving a specimen of his Ability, and, if approv'd, was afterwards call'd a Workhouse keeper.

LONDON. Printed by J. Davis No 10 Brownlow Street Long Acre
Citizen and FRAME-WORK-KNITTER.

14. Broadside 'In Memory of so Great a Genius' printed by J. Davis, Citizen and Frame-Work Knitter. Date unknown.

Began Feb. 1791.

Rev.d M.R LEE, Invent.r 1589.

T HIS is to certify that the *Bearer James Matthews* is full in the Books of the Society of *Ilkiston* and is to all intents and purpofes, a free Brother of the *Fraternity* of FRAME-WORK-KNITTERS.

Feb. 9 1791 *James Chadwick William Brown* STEWARDS.

[Brown, Printer, Leicefter.] *W.m Matthews* CLERK,

15. William Lee's name was incorporated on the membership cards of the Fraternity of Frame-Work Knitters. This card is dated 9 February 1791.

from Spain and Italy. This would also meet the steady increase in demand from French courtiers and nobility.

Situated on the right bank of the Seine, Rouen was renowned in France and abroad as the 'second city of the realm', famous for its ancient merchant marine and commerce, its arts and artists, book-printing and publishing, its industry and long-established activity in textiles. Over several centuries its trade connections within France and with its neighbours in Europe and the Levant, and with England too, revealed an interesting spectrum of goods of its own making: rosaries, chasubles, holy images, vestments for Catholic Spain and Portugal (especially after the peace treaty of 1598), faience and ceramics, clocks, pins, needles, crochet hooks, scissors, thimbles, knitting needles, textiles, stockings, and (according to Declarations of Exportations recorded in 1603) hand-knit stockings of very fine worsted, *façon d'Angleterre*.[7]

Façon d'Angleterre ('of English design') was a term used in a purely qualitative sense to describe the type of stocking that the Rouen workers were hand-knitting. Historical information about the period is available in the records of what was called *Le Tabellionage*, now stored in the Rouen archives, which 'tabulated' acts pursuant to money loans, industrial activity, sales, and items of personal property, etc.

Cited in the same document of the *Tabellionage* is the reference 'stockings of silk' with identification of their makers, 'three English apprentices and Jean Granges, another Englishman . . . who had been employed in the maison[8] of Gédéon Langlois'.[9] Jean Langlois *aiguilletier*[10] was branded a heretic in the sixteenth century and fled from Rouen to England.[11] Some years afterwards Gédéon, kin of

---

[7] *Bulletin de la Commission des Antiquités de la Seine Inférieure, T. XIII: Notes sur d'anciennes Fabriques de Rouen, communication de M. de Beaurepaire.*

[8] Maison = In textiles, in *entreprise libre*, working in own domicile.

[9] M. de Beaurepaire: op. cit.

[10] *Aiguilletier:* Maker of *aiguilletes*, the ends used to fasten garments on the chest or shoulder; point-maker.   [11] Haag: op. cit.

S.Q.—K

Jean, returned to Rouen where he employed '*Jean Granges,
Anglais apprenti*'. Later '*Jehan Grangyer et ouvriers Anglois*'
were to enter the life of William Lee himself in his association with Pierre de Caux. The entry '*de Caux b. Roane*'
appears frequently in the registers of the French Huguenot
churches in England.[12]

In addition to the export of worsted stockings (*bas
d'estame*) as made in the Maison Langlois at Rouen, evidence
of the State's effort to develop its own wares is contained in
an item of the *Tabellionage* dated 1605, '*Fabriqués à Rouen
des bas de soie pour expédier en Espagne*.[13] The story of stockings was now a tale in reverse, indicating the success of
Laffemas's policy; money was no longer leaving France to
pay for the luxury item, 'silk hand-knit stockings from
Spain'. Also, the Conseil du Commerce was noting that
French money was not going out for *bas d'estame* (worsted
stockings) from England, nor for the silk hand-knit stockings imported from Milan and Genoa in Italy.[14]

All this William Lee will have learnt with the keenest
interest from the two brothers de Caux and the fugitive
weavers and merchants who shuttled back and forth from
Rouen and Dieppe to England. He no doubt heard many
stories of their native home, called the 'Manchester of
France'. Especially spectacular was the scene of the Rouen
Halles, the market-place, where in its vast depots were
handled the French woven cloth of every texture and colour,
including the famed *Rouenneries* which was loomed exclusively in Rouen. In dramatic descriptions of the *Hallage*, he
would have been glad to hear that goods of foreign make
were also displayed. Perhaps, from their account of the
weekly buying and selling sessions in the *Halles*, he pondered the challenge when the 'seller of animated eye' met
the 'buyer of calculated eye' . . . a sight, they said, 'to over-
whelm the staidness of any Englishman'.[15] With interest

---

[12] *Huguenot Society Publications.*
[13] E. Gosselin: *Documents Authentiques et Inédits* Rouen (1869).
[14] Boissonade: op cit.   [15] M. Dibdin: *Voyage en Normandie* Rouen.

he will have listened to information relating to Rouen's province, Saint Sever, where spinning, silk-weaving, woollen and linen cloth, bleaching and dyeing works were situated.

It was a heartening experience for the 'decayed artesmaster' from the welfare-shop, Bridewell, to find himself associating with industrialists from Rouen. For the de Caux brothers, too, as Notables of Rouen implementing the efforts of the Conseil to establish new industries, the *genie industriel* of the entrepreneur welcomed the *connaisance speciales* of an inventor such as William Lee. The possibility of developing his invention in France, since in England it faced problems of royal favour and difficulty with the guilds, will have appealed to both sides.

Lee will have been particularly interested in the system of *entreprise libre* that was practised in Rouen at that time. Hand-knitters in the Rouen *faubourgs* le Hurepoix, Dourdan and Étampes, who were engaged in adding woollen and silk stockings (*façon d'Angleterre*) to France's exports, were working in *entreprise libre*. This system of work was 'free' from the guild jurisdiction which had increasingly extended its abuses. Labouring in their own houses with materials fetched by themselves from warehouses, or assigned by city merchants or supported by the *entrepreneur privé*,[16] they were virtually free except that they had to offer a product that reached standards of quality laid down by the Conseil du Commerce's rules as a way of raising the quality of merchandise in the teeth of foreign competition.[17]

Entreprise libre developed widely as an alternative system to the State's regimentation of the guilds and the guilds' tyranny of workers. Neither the privately patronized form of industry that was being extended, nor the guild power that had been torn by the State, were able to prevent the

---

[16] *Entrepreneur privé* is someone active in the direction of an enterprise accorded by the State with some protectionist measures, and which does not receive special privileges.

[17] Boissonade: op. cit.

oppressed and the dispossessed on the lower rung of the industrial hierarchy from seeking increasingly to work on their own account in domiciles.[18] Rouen led among French cities, in having a numerical superiority of trades-free (*métiers libres*) over trades guild-controlled (*métiers jurés*); for those of small tenant status, those oppressed by guild inequities, and for women, girls, and small wage-workers in agriculture, 'free work' was available—predominantly in silk-weaving and cloth-making, and in wool and silk stocking-knitting which maintained 10,000 workers in Le Hurepoix, Rouen.

Laffemas, in charge of the Conseil du Commerce, opposed this regime of work so alien to a regulated and hierarchial industrial society. He denounced '*le métier libre*' as a '*foyer de licence*' and '*d'anarchie économique*'.[19]

However, consideration of inventions, foreign as well as French, was in the proceedings of the Conseil's commission and Lee could not have failed to have been impressed with information from de Caux that under projects for further study was a 'machine for spinning in a single workshop a great quantity of all kinds of wool and other materials by small children, the blind, the aged . . . all seated without bodily work and effort'.[20]

The significance for Lee in this description was that new invention was being recognized in France without the fear and superstition that its introduction was exposed to in England. He would take heart especially from the favourable attitude towards the inventions of foreigners. He could not have realized that Laffemas's mercantilist policy, which welcomed skilled foreigners with knowledge of some new method, was tied essentially to the Commerce General's plan of making the process exclusively a part of France's industrial heritage.

In his *Reiglement Général*, Laffemas was explicit in prohibiting the importing of articles of foreign provenance:

---

[18] Ibid.   [19] Ibid.
[20] Henri Hauser: *Histoire de France*. Livre 1er (1925).

We (the King) prohibit and forbid the entry into our
kingdom of all merchandise, products, manufactures
made and worked up, coming from foreigners, whether
it be cloth of gold, silke, textiles in general, all products
used . . . ornaments and clothing.[21]

Economic xenophobia so deep that penalties for violation
included confiscation of foreign-made goods and the banish-
ment or hanging of the entrepreneur, would have shocked
William Lee. He would have worried that in the new plan
to restore commerce to France the Catholic-Huguenot conflicts still persisted. By contrast when England was the haven
for large numbers of Protestants exiled from Flanders and
France, it was the Elizabethan government that aimed
to keep open doors not unfriendly to the 'straungers',
even though they competitively interfered with native
English employment and were the object of loud protests
from the local guilds who passed stringent rules against
them.

Laffemas's dictum that 'foreign commerce could not be
gainful for France unless there was a stop to the robbery
and trickery received from foreign manufactures' increasingly
sounded like an expression of a persecution complex: 'they
were a bad lot, corrupt, dishonest, immoral, that their
presence in France would only tend to degrade the French
who were normally innocent and honourable'. So pervasive
was the notion that trading with the foreigner was a threat
to the economic salvation of France—circulated through
government assemblies, the *Cahiers*[22] of the French Estates
General, and pamphlets—that anonymous writers also added
their voices, proposing a tax on French exports, so exposing
the foreign land to higher prices and impairment of its

---

[21] B. Laffemas: *Reiglement Général pour Dresser les Manufactures* Paris
(1604–1610).

[22] Cahiers = Statement of grievances for reform, drawn up by the representatives of each estate . . . the nobility, the clergy, the commons. French
Estates General: Comprising representatives of the three estates who made up
the French Parliament.

prosperity. They urged a cold welcome to the foreign entrepreneurs unless they came to buy French manufactured goods and paid in money not in goods, and restrictions upon the enterprises of foreigners within France to prevent them retiring with their 'ill-gotten gains' to their home-land.[23]

If William Lee detected the anonymous voice in the *Advis au Roi* expressing bias against the foreigner, that 'to take his ill-gotten gains out of France was to take bread out of the mouths of the French, wherewith to feed foreigners', he would have been reminded perhaps of the voice of his Calverton neighbours charging that his 'loome to knitte would take the bread out of the mouths of honest hand-knitters'.[24] He would have reflected that in Calverton the attitudes of hostility grew out of fear of future insecurity, while in France it was the harvest of war's ravages.

The momentous decision under the influence of the de Caux brothers to move his looms into France was taken by William Lee in the year 1608 or 1609. Despite admittance to the Weavers Company and successs at long last in his endeavour to obtain Freedom of the City, he will have realized that with the deaths of his patron Lord Hunsdon and of the Queen herself the time was not ripe in England to prosper further with his invention.

William Lee could have been but hopeful that Henry IV's Edict of Nantes would offer freedom to pray and to trade to those of the Reformed religion, a hope that was shared by many exiles from Normandy who hopefully returned home to enjoy religious and civil rights, 'without being examined, molested or troubled to do anything in matters of religion against their consciences'.

It was a progressive France that impressed the inventor because it did not refuse to show interest in labour-saving devices, contrasting with the attitude prevailing in England. Laffemas himself conferred with patrons of inventors, with promoters of enterprises, and reformers of industrial regimes.

23 Boissonade: op. cit.
24 Anonymous authorship: *Advis au Roi*.

The Duc de Sully, prime minister to Henry IV, who originally opposed sericulture in France, now accepted the establishment of manufactures of silks and fine cloths, and entrepreneurs of sericulture actually dedicated their pamphlets to his wife, the Duchess. Numerous applicants came to Paris to demonstrate before Sully and his assistants, who decided on the merits of their inventions and made recommendations of exclusive privileges. Royalty in France served as an instrument for the protection of the inventor and rewarded the spirit of enterprise not only with privilege but with pension.

Even if Lee heard about the dictatorial administration of Laffemas, he would have welcomed many aspects of the French economic theorist's pronouncements on the idle poor; the tenet that 'work was the law of the universe' would seem to cast the Huguenot Laffemas in the image of a Puritanical Huguenot, voicing the same doctrines as Cambridge's preacher Perkins, 'that God gave men various kinds of work to prevent idleness'. The mercantilist's claim for his policy that 'it would serve, through the establishment of manufactures, to drive away idleness . . . and employ and support the poor' will have made the divinity-trained inventor consider that his English loom was destined to play a part in the economic regeneration of France.

He would hope that his introduction of a new method would be as fruitful to manufactures in the 'promised land' as the contributions of French and Dutch exiles were in the history of Norwich and other 'decayed' towns in his native land: 'Norwich and other towns grew rich by the new way of trade the strangers taught them, of *bayes, sayes, arras* and *mogadoes*,[25] which hath not used to be made in this our realm of England.'[26]

When William Lee arrived in France in 1608 or 1609, the domain of the *entreprise libre* was considerable. He will

---

[25] *Bayes, sayes, arras, mogadoes* = various types of woollen cloths.
[26] S. J. Burn: *History of Foreign Protestant Refugees settled in England* (1846).

have found in Rouen, where the manufacture of hand-knit stockings of silk and wool was flourishing, the greatest interest in his machine as a way of expanding trade. Laffemas himself had written, 'only 30 years after Henry II wore silk stockings, 50,000 people wear out 4 pairs yearly, at a cost of 4 écus a pair . . . thus 800,000 écus leave France for one import item of dress'.

The merchants of Rouen and the Conseil du Commerce itself will have had the highest hopes that the Englishman's machine would tip the balance of trade.

Above all, William Lee will have looked forward to his new calling in France as the land of Henry IV, architect of the Edict of Nantes, with an avowed aim of building peace in the name of religious freedom; a land nourished by the cosmopolitanism of its prime minister Sully, in counter-attitude to the anti-foreign bias of Laffemas. From the creative point of view, Lee would have been greatly excited at the news that Henry had proposed to Sully the plan of an institution in Paris to serve as a *Musée de Machines*.[27] No doubt he had the confidence that his own machine would soon be honoured there.

Within a few years, however, a tragic event occurred which once again confounded the inventor's fortunes.

---

[27] Boissonade: op. cit.

ELEVEN

The de Caux-Lee Contract

IF historians have assumed that the rewards of success totally
eluded the curate-inventor during his lifetime, it is due to
the fact that the full story of his activity was unknown until
comparatively recently. Lying dormant for centuries in the
Archives de la Seine Maritime was a document disclosing
a contract dated 1611:

> ... for the manufacture of stockings of silk and of wool
> on the machine, at present introduced in the realm, by
> the inventor Lee . . .[1]

That this important documentation of Lee's record of
endeavour did not come to light for nearly 300 years seems
to point to the national rivalry entertained by France towards
England in the field of invention. The contract, between
William Lee and Pierre de Caux, was still seemingly buried
from view and knowledge when in 1656 a native of Nîmes
succeeded in secretly entering England and taking back a
memory picture of the first knitting loom, for reproducing
it piece by piece in France.[2] Still undisclosed was the
document crediting the English loom-inventor when in 1696
a French government decreed that the makers of *bas au
métier*[3] should form *une communauté particulière*.[4]

It was almost three centuries later, in 1888, that the

---

[1] The original contract is in the Archives de la Seine Maritime, Rouen,
France. *Tabelliones de Rouen, Meubles,* 2nd Series. March 30, 1611.

[2] Diderot's *Encyclopaedia*: Jean Hindret entrusted with mission to spy out
secret of the English knitting loom.

[3] Bas au métier = Loom-knit stockings.

[4] M. E. Gosselin: *Memoir Précité.* Arrêt du Conseil, Dec. 22, 1696,
ordered the formation of a special guild for loom-knitters.

138   STOCKINGS FOR A QUEEN

Archivist Charles de Beaurepaire, addressing the Commission des Antiquités in Rouen, presented as a '*découverte
historique*', the de Caux-Lee contract.[5]

The contract that he revealed is signed by Lee and by
de Caux, with the signatories identified as Guillaume Lee
'*gentilhomme Anglois*' and Pierre de Caux '*bourgeois de Rouen*',
and attested by the *Tabelliones*.[6] Penned in old French in
1611, the survival of this *traité* for the manufacture of
stockings of silk and of wool unlocks knowledge of the
inventor's life-story.

In the Lee-de Caux contract, signed in Rouen, there is
a provision which refers to a 'wife':

> If Lee should happen to die, before the 19 years of the
> contract is completed, the same association will be
> continued with his wife or heirs.

If it is accepted that this provision was inserted in the
contract for future contingencies, as related to foreign per-
sonnel engaged in new industries who settled in France, then
it bears out the generally accepted assumption that the
inventor never married.

By the time Lee arrived in Rouen late in 1608, Laffemas,
head of the Conseil had approved and disapproved a number
of proposals, as well as inventions.[7] Some projects like silk
culture were 'dear to his heart . . . in his position of power
and control',[8] though he was inveighing against 'envious
foreigners' who threw into the dyeing kettle pots of tar,
spoiling all the French-made silks. In Laffemas's appraisal
the demon was the 'corrupt foreigner' whereas Lee will have
recognized fear of competition and loss of trade.

What was life like in Rouen for Lee when he arrived?
He had the great advantage that he was the direct associate

---

[5] *Commission des Antiquités de la Seine Inférieure. Tome VIII Ire Livraison.*
[6] De Caux-Lee Contract: See Appendix 'C'.
[7] The Conseil du Commerce later functioned as the 'Commission Consulta-
tive sur le faict du commerce général et de l'establissement des Manufactures'.
[8] P. Boissonade: *Le Socialisme d'État (1443–1661)* Paris (1927).

of such notables as Salomon and Pierre de Caux. They were numbered among the royal patrons whom the King recruited from high clergy, nobility, sheriffs, and the most influential and alert citizens of every town. Salomon de Caux became known to Laffemas through consultations on engineering projects in Paris[9] and known to the King who titled him *Ingénieur du Roi*, and aided him in the publication of his first important work.[10]

Through the influence of the Pierre de Caux Lee became a protégé of the prime minister, Sully, who received him with favour and was so impressed with his invention that it was said he gave him means to construct new looms.[11] Being thus accredited the contract with Pierre de Caux to introduce loom-knitting of stockings in France was reconfirmed on his arrival.

Lee will have been immensely impressed to discover in Paris that the King himself, in an elaborate State-coach accompanied by his courtiers regularly visited such places as silk manufactures in the Place Royale; the studios of the Louvre where worked painters, sculptors, tapestry-makers; the silk plantations in his own royal gardens; his parks with silk-workrooms; and the spinning mills in the Tuileries. This royal activity reflected the State's participation in industrial enterprises of an artistic and luxury character, achieved through a system of grants of all kinds to its royal entrepreneurs. Subsidies took the form of gifts or loans without interest, even of lodgings in the Louvre and in the Tuileries at the expense of the State.[12] The State's endeavour was based on its proclamation in 1602 that 'there was nothing as advantageous . . . as the manufactures that attract men and riches'.

In Rouen Lee found the merchants in highest praise of their 'industries indigènes': silks, linens, woollens. Again,

[9] J. Pannier: *L'Église Reformée de Paris sous Henrei IV* Paris (1911).
[10] Salomon de Caux: *La Perspective avec la Raison des Ombres et Miroirs* (1612).
[11] Alfred Renouard: *Traité complet de Bonneterie Mécanique* Paris (1921).
[12] Boissonade: op. cit.

the King's hand was evident in the Wolf and Lambert, and Pinchon manufacturies flourishing in the Rouen province of Saint Sever. The Flemish entrepreneurs, Wolf and Lambert, had successfully sought royal privileges to make linens *façon d Hollande*, claiming that in their ability to undercut the cost of the Dutch product there would be increased sales with the benefit of increased export taxes to the King.[13] Significantly, the Commission's recommendation to Henry IV for a grant emphasized that, through the Wolf and Lambert enterprise, Catholic Franco-Spanish trade would gain at the expense of Dutch-Spanish trade.

Similarly, the Pinchon application to introduce the treatment of fustians *façon d'Angleterre*, through the recruitment of an Englishman Charles Morice from Suffolk to teach the English method, was also granted a ten-year privilege. Again, it was enunciated that its usefulness to the State would be to further cultivate Franco-Spanish relations in opposition to the Protestant English.

Details such as these will not have been known to Lee until much later, if at all. Much of the work conducted by Laffemas and his Conseil du Commerce was necessarily secretive. Even a special *Reiglement* for the manufacture of stockings of silk and wool, prepared by Laffemas, was not published.[14]

If there were the element of secrecy it may relate to an earlier contract concerning Lee's looms, referred to in the 1611 de Caux contract: that four other looms (*'les autres 4 mestiers'*) were delivered (*'livrés'*), as negotiated in the first contract (*'le premier traicté'*).[15] The missing document, the 'first contract', constitutes a gap in the course of French economic history. In the words of the archivist . . . 'there are *lagunes* (gaps) in the documents of the Archives due to diverse circumstances'.[16]

---

[13] *Tabellionage de Rouen* 29 Mars 1607.   [14] Boissonade: op. cit.
[15] De Caux-Lee Contract: see Appendix 'C'.
[16] *Archives des Services de la Seine Maritime:* Documents in Archives Register, *'Heritages et Meubles'* missing for 1604.

That the course of William Lee's life was also marked by 'diverse circumstances' is gleaned from a *Tabellionage* entry:

> . . . Stockings of silk made in Rouen in the *maison* of Gédéon Langlois . . . mention of *3 anglais apprentis*, where another Englishman, named Jean Granges, had also been employed. . . . *Contract de I er Mars.* 1604.[17]

The Rouen *Tabellionage* item simply refers to a contract: it makes no reference, as does the 1611 de Caux-Lee contract, to '4 other looms' and a missing document. It does refer, however, to '3 *anglais apprentis*', specifically one Jean Granges whose name can be identified with one of the *'ouvriers anglois'* named in the 1611 de Caux-Lee contract. Thus, the reference to English workers, including Jean Grangyer (Jean Granges), links the contracts of March 1604, and of 1611 between the entrepreneur Pierre de Caux and the inventor William Lee.

The missing document, comprising the first contract, must have related to the *Maison Langlois* wherein *industrie libre* and the manufacture of hand-knit stockings flourished. As already described, this form of labour, denounced by Laffemas as *'d'anarchie économique'*, acutely increased the State's dilemma. It involved the State directly with the multitudes of hand-workers in Rouen who were engaged in stocking-knitting, a commodity with a considerable market. It made the State hesitate to back inventors with capital support because the stocking-market without guild wardenship was undercutting prices at home and abroad.[18] In such a situation the repression of the *entreprise libre* was marked in fact by considerable restraint on the part of the State though still countered by its police authority. Did Pierre de Caux, who held *'une position importante en qualité industriel'* in Rouen, realize in 1604 that the time was not right for the

---

[17] *Tabellionage de Rouen*, reported by M. F. Gosselin: *Notes sur d'Anciennes Fabriques de Rouen.*   [18] Boissonade: op. cit.

successful introduction of the '*métier mécanique inventé par le pasteur Lee*'.[19]

Four years later, in 1608, Lee was to learn that the *Maison Langlois*, as a unit in domiciled industry, had grown against the State's extension of monopoly in guild management, with its attendant abuses of the apprentice and journeyman. Especially in Rouen there was a preponderance of '*métiers libres*'.[20] The labour system was showing progressive changes from the day when workers fetched materials and bought tools on their own account, extending now to financing operations by *marchand entrepreneurs* (merchant entrepreneurs).[21] That it was characterized by a third feature in its operation—financial support by an entrepreneur *privé* who was *privileged* in terms of his access to some State protectionist provisions but deprived of the special privileges granted to the royal entrepreneurs—was revealed in the 1611 de Caux-Lee contract. Evidence from two sources—the nature of the provisions of the 1611 contract and the identification of the English workers in the *Maison Langlois*—suggests that the silk-merchant, Pierre de Caux, was the *marchand-entrepreneur* and that the *Maison Langlois* was the sub-contractor in the enterprise of hand-knit stockings *façon d'Angleterre*.[22]

February 10, 1611, must have been a memorable day for William Lee when the signing of the contract was witnessed for a 'company organized for manufacturing stockings of silk and of wool, upon a loom to be presently introduced in this country.'[23] Gratifying to the inventor was the fact that the document expressed faith in his loom, with acknowledgement of 'four machines already delivered'; gratifying to the Englishman were the provisions reflecting the integrity of this important French citizen and Huguenot with whom he

---

[19] C. de Beaurépaire: *Notes sur Salomon de Caux* (1888). *Bulletin de la Commission des Antiquités de la Seine Inférieure, T.VIII.*

[20] *Métiers libres* = Trades served by labour, free of guild wardenship.

[21] Boissonade: op. cit.   [22] Gosselin: op. cit.

[23] De Caux-Lee Contract: see Appendix 'C'.

was to be associated. Pierre de Caux was known as a man 'of words as good as his bond'.

As the entrepreneur, de Caux shared Lee's concern at the State's authoritative policy vis-à-vis protection of royal entrepreneurs and guild management at the cost of repression of workers. Hence arose his intention to organize a *société privée*, not one with royal initiative.[24] The type of enterprise was *collectivité*: Pierre de Caux and the 'honourable gentlemen' Nicholas de Format and Jacques Le Tartier would provide the financing, and William Lee the contribution of his name and effort by virtue of his loom. The associates were to be *'par obligation insollido et sans division'* (with joint and equal obligations).

The 1611 de Caux-Lee contract reveals that the inventor had been installed at Rouen with his eight machines and that Sully's petition to obtain the monopoly for him had been received graciously by the King. To the curate-inventor, confidence and hope were returning. He had found a kindred soul in Pierre de Caux, who came from a Huguenot family that included both pastors and inventors. Lee was pleased no doubt that Pierre's two brothers, Salomon and Isaac, who were both illustrious in engineering and creative fields, had accredited his loom.[25] They, too, had been oppressed by Catholic doctrines and had been given Biblical names in secret protest, which will have reassured Lee. Pierre also was very strongly identified with the Protestant religion.[26] His election as *Conseiller au Roi* (5 fevrier 1607) will have impressed Lee though he may have been concerned as to the reason for his voluntary resignation from the appointment to the *office titulaire*, which precluded his installation.[27]

In the de Caux-Lee contract *'Guillaume Lee, gentilhomme anglois'* is named *'autheur'* (inventor) and *'maistre conduisant*

[24] Boissonade: op. cit.
[25] Christina S. Maks: *Salomon de Caux, le fameux Ingénieur, Architecte et Musicien* (1935).
[26] P. Le Gendre: *Histoire de Persécution Faite à L'Église de Rouen* (1874).
[27] Archives Départmentales de la Seine Inférieure: *Serie B. Memoriaux de la Cour des Aides, tome 16 feuillets 96, 97.*

de manufacture' (head of manufacture). After the years of persevering work, marked by hope, promise, and disappointment, he was eager to fulfil the assignment in the contract: 'to supply 32 additional machines, besides the eight already delivered'. His productivity both in London and Rouen was revealed and confirmed in the statement:

> I, (Lee) shall be obligated to supply 4 machines, in good condition . . . and the other 4 . . . following the first contract with the said de Caux.

Related to his obligation to 'supply 6 English workers . . . skilled', there was a protective attitude in the provisions. They were to be furnished . . . 'liberties', 'bonuses', 'monthly compensation' and, significantly, there was recognition of the workers' services performed 'for the benefit of the company . . . for the last 4 looms supplied heretofore', with payment to Lee to meet the arrears. He was grateful that de Caux shared his feeling of the rights and dignity of the worker.

In the 'We, Pierre de Caux' opening of the contract the entrepreneur met the requirement, still current, as publicized by Laffemas in 1609, that 'the management of all commercial enterprises was not to be entrusted to foreigners, but to native Frenchmen'.[28] This was intrinsic to the State policy that, though it recruited foreign skilled workers and inventors with knowledge of new methods, the required preference was for native French. Lee's teaching obligations included the clauses:

> To teach the operation of his loom . . . to teach how to build and dismantle the loom . . . to teach others how to teach . . .

Additional was the stipulated responsibility:

> To teach the secret of manufacturing these looms, without concealing anything whatsoever.

[28] B. Laffemas: *Comme l'on Permettre* (1609).

16. First page from the original document incorporating the de Caux-Lee contract, dated 10 February 1611.

17. Rouen in the sixteenth century, from P. A. Floquet's *Anecdotes Normandes* (Rouen, 1883).

The latter regulation underwrote the authority of the State that knowledge of new methods contributed by foreigners should belong to French industry; it was also in the spirit of Laffemas 'that no foreigner, especially English, was to be trusted'.[29] However, there was a distinction in this provision of the contract for although the factor of restriction imposed by the State was implicit in 'I, (Lee) will be obligated to teach as large a number of apprentices as there will be looms made, but no more', there was no stated penalty for the violation of the requirement of secrecy. In the Pinchon contract, on the other hand, a fine of 300 livres was stipulated as a way of penalizing the English worker recruited from Suffolk if he revealed the secret of the new process for the treatment of fustians.[30]

An ambiguous limitation is implied relative to the contract provision that offers to Lee:

> . . . advance of loans or provisions monthly for the looms and engines . . . provided the aforesaid associates have not had them made better themselves.

The conditioning clause, 'provided the aforesaid associates have not had them made better themselves', in a strict sense would seem to nullify the spirit of the contract as pertinent to the *advance of loans to Lee . . . for the looms and engines*. If interpreted in the context of the liberal terms of the contract, with the promoter de Caux favouring Lee and his English workers, the evidence would then suggest that the de Caux associates permitted the voiding clause in order to conform to the authority of the State as vested in the Commission's function.[31]

Even in the light of the State's regulations and its limitations of grants of privileges to the enterprise privée, care was taken that the well-being of the foreign inventor was not exploited as evidenced by the all-inclusive contract

---

[29] Boissonade: op. cit. [30] *Tabellionage de Rouen*: op. cit.

[31] Functions of the Commission—To consult with and regulate the contracts of the promoters of enterprises.

S.Q.—L

formulated by de Caux for a '*société insolludo et sans division*'.
This must have reminded Lee of the preachment of William
Perkins, 'free of greed and fraudulent dealing', thus free of
a 'grave sin'.[32] In addition to the 2500 livres as payment for
indebtedness for delivered looms and past labour, Lee would
be furnished:

> Rent of quarters, supply of silk and wool, wages for
> hired help and labour, lodgings and food for workers,
> advance of loan . . . or monthly provision for the looms
> and engines.

In the actual functioning of the organized company, 'to
commence work at the manufacture, on the day following
the Feast of the Annunciation 1610', financial equity is
stipulated for the inventor both in income and profit-sharing:
'. . . for the income and profit is to be shared equally of which
one share shall be for Lee'.

Lee was treated fairly, or even favoured, in relation to
such contingencies as a failure to find markets for their
product. 'Lee . . . to be exempt from making advances or to
contribute to the proportion of his ownership.' The case of
work-stoppage was covered by: 'Lee . . . to be paid 75 livres,
for each week of default . . . this to be for particular interest
of Lee and not paid to any other.'

In the event of failure of the company before the end of
the twenty-year association period it was laid down: '. . . the
looms will be shared between the associates and Lee; in this
situation, Lee would be obligated to pay his share'.

In the management of the enterprise de Caux, the contract
provided for accounting procedures at intervals to secure
honest adjustment of profits. This clause may well have
convinced Lee that the '*droit committimus*'[33] accorded to Wolf
and Lambert and other royal entrepreneurs, a privilege he

---

[32] William Perkins: *Workes I*.
[33] *Droit Committimus* = The right granted by the King to bring an action
before special judges.

considered unjust, would not be needed here even though this State grant was denied to the entrepreneur-privé.

In passing it is noteworthy that the English workers under the de Caux associates were precluded from availing themselves of free beer in a beer-garden, a privilege that Wolf and Lambert were granted with other fiscal grants from the State.

As the English inventor was concerned at the welfare of his workers, he was pleased no doubt that they 'were to be given the rights of all Frenchmen', and that they were to be accorded liberty, 'free to depart from this country . . . without expense . . . or restitution of monies by Lee'. That this 'freedom' to depart did not carry the usual penalty of imprisonment and the harsher penalties meted to deserters was gratifying, but Lee will have been sobered as he realized that the 'escape' clause was in the event of two contingencies: the enterprise being served a writ; or, in its dissolution, when 'failing to make a profit, in the ratio of 10 to 100'.

In the event of the dissolution, as 'it shall be the right of each one in the association to withdraw', he perhaps wondered about the clause 'but Lee shall be entirely free to manufacture for his own account, or to stop as he wishes'. As the months passed William Lee did not lose his trust in Pierre de Caux but he had increasing doubts and anxieties about France itself. There was protection in the one but premonition in the other. His attitude was one of gratitude for the royal protection accorded him as an inventor but, sensitive to injustice, he was concerned that the royal prerogatives extended to entrepreneurs exempting them from ordinary jurisdiction in allowing them the law of 'droit committimus'. His questioning attitude was identified with William Perkins's charge against 'abusers of honest vocations' through the means of 'unjust magistrates, grasping lawyers, dishonest traders'.[34]

Moreover, the skilled worker, who had been enticed to privileged industry under royal authority by promises of

[34] William Perkins: *A Treatise of the Vocations or Callings of Man* (1603).

benefits and fiscal advantages, with his place in the first rank of the hierarchy of fellow workers, found it was at the cost of iron discipline. The worker, who fled from the tyrannies of the guild to labour *libre*, found he did not even receive the franchises accorded to the workers of the royal enterprises. If he were caught in violation of any local regulation, he was without any safeguard against administrative authority; under police discipline, he could not escape from the penalties meted out by the guilds, which were the very authorities he had sought to escape in his turning to labour *libre*.[35]

Identified with the plight of the worker, William Lee, an accredited inventor, began to feel alien in his adopted land. In his native land, did not the scales tip more fairly for the worker? There the Justices of the Peace were called upon to rate wages in districts each year; there were frequent wage assessments in Spitalfields affecting spinners and weavers of yarns of various qualities, and for cloth of various sizes.[36] In France, maximum wage rates were established by the King's advisors and, when the worker complained or took higher wages, orders went out to the sheriffs and royal officers to inflict strict fines, whippings, imprisonment . . . even death.

The Englishman began to question the laudible efforts for the restoration of industry in France, carried out at such a cost to the majority of the population made up of artisans, lower middle-class shopkeepers, the small trader, a group with whom he ever felt kinship. In addition to the *taille*[37] it was the onslaught of the *gabelle*,[38] the Crown's most lucrative source of revenue, that oppressed the poor who had to cut their savings to the bone in order to take up their quota of salt at inflated prices. He was increasingly troubled by the fact that the clergy and nobility escaped from the burden of paying taxes—taxes levied on the poorer classes to make the

---

[35] Boissonade: op. cit.
[36] *Calendar of State Papers: Domestic. Elizabeth.* CCXIV. No. 130.
[37] *Taille* = various consumer taxes.
[38] *Gabelle* = Salt tax.

luxury products that Laffemas had proclaimed as essential to embellish the castles and palaces of the nobility and royal family.[39]

But his main fear grew from a tragic event that took place even before he signed the contract, presaging an end to the brief age of progress in France that had so attracted him there from his native land. In 1610 Henry IV of France was assassinated by Ravaillac in Paris.[40] Before long, added to the anti-foreigner bias of Laffemas, was the return of a religious intolerance that was to nullify the inventor's dearest hopes.

[39] C. Wolsey Cole: *French Mercantilist Doctrines before Colbert* (1931).
[40] Georges Théry: *Recueil des Actes de la Vénérable Marie de Poussepin* Tours (1938).

TWELVE

'The Loome Returns'

LEE's deep discouragement at the assassination of Henry IV
was shared by de Caux. They both recognized that the clock,
ticking religious freedom since the Edict of Nantes, was
threatened with another set-back. The policy of Henry IV
to grant the Huguenots civil and political rights formerly
refused them by the Catholics would be violated as economic
need and want excited the clamours of the more violent
factions.

In the last years of Henry's reign the anti-foreigner bias
of Laffemas had reverted to religious bias in others. As the
State's authorized inequities in the economic sphere grew,
the reformed religion received less and less consideration as
a religion equal with that of the State. Pierre de Caux,
perhaps due to his concern with the growing danger of the
injustices and inequities, had resigned from his office
titulaire of *Conseiller au roi*. Lee's apprehension at the time,
though he did not fully understand the causes, was justified.

None the less, de Caux's industrial standing in Rouen and
his relationship to the celebrated Salomon, *ingénieur du roi*,
had qualified him effectively in securing acceptance as a
promoter of an *entreprise privé*. The subsequent de Caux-
Lee contract showed, even beset with doubts as he was, his
own self-confidence as well as his confidence in Lee, expressed in the phrase '*Je prometz . . .*' As the contract clearly
stated:

> We, the aforesaid de Caux and associates will be
> obligated within six months from this day . . . to give
> Lee these privileges, and to secure him letters of
> nationality for himself . . . these privileges to be verified

at the place necessary without any expense or trouble on his part.[1]

The English inventor had hopefully looked forward to going again to Paris, 'the place necessary' to receive his letters of nationality. He remembered the poignancy of his first visit when he was called forward to be presented by the Duc de Sully to the King for his grant of privileges for his loom. The assassination of Henry IV destroyed the anticipation and plan.

To Lee, who had experienced seemingly endless waits for the acknowledgement of his invention from Lord Hunsdon and the Queen, the 'within six months' period for receipt of the requisite nationality papers would not have seemed too long, especially in the light of the contract's provision for a 'société de manufacture' with its '20 year concession obtained from the King'.

He also found assurance in the thought that Pierre de Caux was of firm character, reflected in his endurance in the past when as a Huguenot in Rouen, excluded from civil and political offices prior to the enactment of the Edict of Nantes, he channelled his energies to both Church and industrial pursuits. The Huguenots, celebrating fewer fast and feast days than the Catholics, worked continuously so there had been in the English-French trade a greater readiness to conduct dealings with them.[2]

Lee realized now that the Rouen industrialist, even prior to and increasingly since the assassination of Henry IV in 1610, viewed with the greatest apprehension the State's extension and control of patronal industries. To Lee's acute intelligence it became clear that the *entrepreneur* de Caux had inserted in the contract those particular clauses relating to optional departure from France in order to protect him and his English workers not only simply from anti-foreigner restrictions but from the vicissitudes of a worsening economic

---

[1] De Caux-Lee Contract: see Appendix 'C'.

[2] Samuel Smiles: *The Huguenots, their Settlement, Churches and Industry in England* (1868).

climate. In Rouen the unemployed thronged the welfare workshops, from whence came the forced labour in the textiles field including the *bonneterie*.[3] For the flourishing stocking-market there was a labour supply far exceeding the market's demand. The inventor deplored the disheartening experience for the *entrepreneur*. Their joint plan for the enterprise as well as the long-awaited opportunity for his invention seemed thwarted at the start. Once again he seemed to be the right man at the wrong time.

After the assassination, religion increasingly became the instrument of State to meet the demoralization of the worker. Louis XIII, the son and successor of Henry IV, aided the Catholic agitation and the growing pressure of the Monastic orders to form Brotherhoods—a movement designed to maintain religious observances and reverential attitudes in the churches, with attendant penalties of fines, whips and the use of torture for non-conformity.

Soon the requirement to observe Catholic Church attendance was extended to the Huguenots, exposing the worker to the most exigent weapon in religion's name: a choice of conversion to the State church or exclusion of a place in his trade.

William Lee was deeply concerned at the increasing distress of the worker in the land where he had believed that his loom would bring more work. He was mindful of the words of William Perkins that work afforded man would benefit the Church and the commonweal. Deprivation of work was now the threat of the French State; it would use the Church as its tool to discipline the worker with a crucial penalty—no work.

Lee realized that Louis XIII would fully enforce the policy of religious intolerance. At his Coronation he had sworn:

> I shall endeavour . . . to drive from my jurisdiction and from the lands subject to me, all heretics denounced

[3] *Bonneterie* = stocking-knitting.

by the Church . . . so help me God and the Holy Gospels of God.[4]

Lee's fears for the safety of his English workers grew as a placard, posted on the walls of houses in Rouen, confirmed the spirit of the King:

> Poor Catholics! Have a care for yourselves . . . beware of the Huguenots. Visit their homes and disarm them. Let us have good watch . . . be kept ready . . . and at the soonest. We are sleeping and the Huguenot is awake.[5]

The inventor was deeply shocked to discover how the monopoly of the guild-master now gave birth to religious bias. The requirements for apprenticeship had a new base . . . nationality, age, and religion. To the rigours that the State permitted the apprentice to be subjected to—high entrance fees, enforced low salary levels, penalties—it now added the feature of restriction upon national origin and religion, thus leaving the worker with almost no defence in finding a place in his trade. The rights of the journeyman were also in danger. Required to register with the guild, unable to meet the demand of high fees, when he sought to work in his own domicile he was branded by the State's police as a *chambrelan*, subject to harsh penalties. His quest for work was further blocked by the prohibition against rental of quarters to him.[6]

Though Pierre de Caux had not stipulated in the contract the Laffemas requirement (as was part of the Wolf and Lambert, the Pinchon, and other contracts) that one-half of the workers employed be French, none the less the State's course now would be in pursuit of Lee's workers. De Caux's

---

[4] Henry M. Baird: *The Huguenots and the Revocation of the Edict of Nantes* New York (1895).
[5] Ibid: The words of the placard were preserved in the Secret Registers of the Parlement of Rouen in 1611.
[6] P. Boissonade: *Le Socialisme d'État (1453–1661)* Paris (1927).

protective measures would be unavailing to the *ouvriers Anglois*; they would be exposed to harsher measures than the workers with the 'rights of native Frenchmen'. Intolerance, Lee feared, would not only nullify those provisions designed as safeguards by de Caux but would entail penalties.

In France, in this period when the value of the livre had dropped to the sou, the workers' discontent and growing revolt gave birth to a revolutionary organization, the *Compagnonnage*, with the aim of checking widespread unemployment.[7] Among this secret association's aims was the alleviation of the condition of the migratory worker fleeing the intolerances in his trade that drove him from Paris to other cities . . . to Toulouse or Dijon . . . and from other cities to Rouen. Here Lee would have noted its growth, later reaching 30,000.

This coalition of workers, functioning as a union, semi-religious in character, offered money-relief to the victims of work-stoppage and industrial depression. It held meetings to deliberate the workers' betterment, to plot against the abuses of the *entrepreneurs*, and to order strikes against Masters in their workshops so as to enforce an improved level in working conditions and wages. William Lee, identified with the plight of the worker, was encouraged to find that against the invincibility of the guilds and the indifference of the State this force through its solidarity and mutual self-defence was raising its voice and action against long-standing injustices.

It was in Rouen, where the inventor had experienced the ultimate hopes for his loom, that irony was to colour his final days. An essential purpose of the *Compagnonnage* was to monopolize the employment of the hand-worker. Progress in manufacture had been retarded, evidenced in the State's struggle with the syndicates of the *Compagnonnage* and in the guild's hostility to labour-saving machines in this period of mass unemployment. The activity of the *Compagnonnage*

7 William Steares Davis: *History of France* New York (1910).

was moving against the intruder, *le métier*,[8] lest it lessen the availability of places in the trades. The influence of the *Compagnonnage* was demonstrated a short time later when in 1614 the handicraft workers in Paris took an agitated stand for the return of the 'old methods of hand-fabrication'.[9]

All these considerations led Lee finally to take the heart-breaking decision to remove his looms from France. Even then he realized that the escape of his workers with the looms would be difficult and subject to terror such as was experienced during the Catholic-Huguenot conflicts in the long years of religious persecution. His greatest anxiety was that the additional threats would confront his Protestant workers in the perilous exodus from Dieppe to Dover; they would now be suspect as foreigners, and with their looms as trade-secret transgressors, even though the loom was his own brain-child.

William Lee's hope was mixed with prayer for the safety of James and his workers, and the return of the looms to England. He would have been grateful to have known the record of history that, through their safe journey, the foundation of the frame-work knitting industry belonged to his native land. Though the clause in the de Caux-Lee contract that 'William Lee be entirely free to manufacture on his own account' proved to be unrealistic, his brother James and his workers were free to set up the looms in Old Street Square in London. From then onwards the practice of machine-knitting spread throughout the commercial world. Fittingly claimed for Lee's knitting loom was the position in history expressed in the Petition to the Lord Protector, Oliver Cromwell, for the 'Incorporation of the Frame-Work Knitters Guild' on October 25, 1655:

> The trade of frame-work knitting was never known or practised in England . . . or in any other place in the world . . . before it was invented, and found out by

[8] *Métier* = Machine.
[9] Boissonade: op. cit.

one William Lee, of Calverton, in the County of Nottingham.[10]

So ended the inventor's earlier dream of '32 additional machines, besides the 8 already provided for' being installed in Rouen's Saint Sever as stipulated in the de Caux-Lee contract—his dream of joining the other Royal enterprises . . . the *Grande Tissanderie* with 360 weaving looms of the Flemish Wolf and Lambert . . . the large *Atelier* of Paul Pinchon who had recruited an English apprentice to teach the French the secret of treating fustians.

Perhaps the intuitive mind of Lee projected the future questions of the archivist and historian:

> *Que devint de Wolfe & Lambert? . . . et de celle Pinchon?*
> *tant d'éclat a'leur naissance . . . que disparaitre . . . dans*
> *quel catastrophe?*[11]

and the answer to the query from a later archivist:

> *Les diverses industries . . . pratiquèrent a Rouen pendant*
> *Ier tier du 17ième siècle ont plus tard disparu pour cause*
> *de religion.*[12]

History records that William Lee died in Paris '*dans la misère*'. In a broadside to his memory printed by a member of the Frame-Work Knitters Guild, its inscription to the 'Ingenius William Lee . . . but being despised he went to France, yet of iron to himself' reflects the courage and tenacity of the expatriated Englishman—indeed of 'iron' as he sought to go from Rouen to Paris.[13] Sensitive to the finer

[10] The Petition of the Worshipful Company of Frame-Work Knitters, in Charles Deering's *Nottingham, Vetus et Nova* (1751).

[11] Archivist M. E. Gosselin: 'What became of Wolfe & Lambert? And of Pichon? With so much renown to their establishment . . . what catastrophe caused their disappearance?' M. E. Gosselin: *Documents Authentiques et Inédits du Commerce Rouennaise.*

[12] Archivist C. Beaurepaire: 'Various industries that functioned in Rouen, in the first part of the 17th century, later disappeared because of religion'. C. Beaurepaire: *Bulletin de la Commission des Antiquités de la Seine Inférieure.*

[13] *Broadside,* printed by J. Davis, Citizen and Frame-Work Knitter.

work his looms could make, he recalled perhaps that three months after the Duc de Sully had favoured his invention he had made a gift of the first twelve pairs of stockings, *fabriqués au métier en France*, to Marie de Medici.[14]

The gift had pleased her and he may have considered now the importance of pleading with the Queen Regent concerning the dangers besetting France. In Paris, discord had long broken loose. Embittered by the old religious animosities, civil war had broken out between the Court and the country factions.[15]

But the Queen had no time for William Lee. Joined by her son, Louis XIII, she was again the bitter enemy of Protestantism. Lee found himself quite alone as he learned that Sully had become suspect, had lost his power and influence, and had resigned and retired to his estate in Rosney.[16] [17]

So passed William Lee, the curate-inventor, and the misery of his last days may have been also in his realization that the efforts of France to build industrial enterprise had failed. France had first frustrated its people in its failure to build peace through religious freedom. The lines of the poet, John Milton, may have confirmed his thoughts:

> *Yet sometimes nations will decline so low*
> *From vertue, which is reason, that no wrong*
> *But Justice, and some fatal curse annext,*
> *Deprives them of their outward libertie,*
> *Their inward lost.*

In England, at about the same time as the archivist's recovery of the de Caux-Lee contract took place in France,

[14] George Théry: *Recueils des Actes de la Vénérable Marie Poussepin* Tours (1938).
[15] Smiles: op. cit.
[16] *Memoirs of the Duke of Sully*: Edinburgh Edition (1819).
[17] That Sully was in danger is related to the printing of his Memoirs. In the original edition the title page gave the fictitious name of the alleged printers as the author, and located the place of publication in Amsterdam, in place of Rosny, France, where it was printed.

William Lee received from a great institution of learning due recognition of the genius of his invention. In 1882, three centuries after his graduation from Cambridge, his Alma Mater erected to the memory of 'Gulielmus Lee' a stained-glass window in Christ's College.

He is holding in his hand neither the book of the scholar, the sword of the soldier, nor the crucifix of the church, as other worthies of the university are shown. He simply holds a model of the knitting loom he invented, a tribute of the university to the man and to the importance of his contribution to mankind.

In a very real sense William Lee was the father of the machine-wrought knit-goods industry; the loom he created was its genesis, the basis of all subsequent inventions for the knitting of textiles. In the movement from handicrafts to machine operation, its course was beset with the problem of the expendability of man versus the machine. The history of the 'loome to knitte' manifested that the 'web of our life is of a mingled yarn, good and ill together'.[18]

Invention has its martyrs no less than religion. Religion shaped and claimed William Lee. The loom that he made indeed carried threads in its web that were vulnerable to the Fates with their shears. Its survival is by virtue of the needles of his genius.

[18] Shakespeare: *All's Well that Ends Well*, Act IV.

WILL AND PROBATE OF WILLIAM LEE

OF CALVERTON, YEOMAN

(The father of William Lee, the Inventor)

In the name of God, Amen; the 16th day of April, Anno Domini, 1607. I, William Lee, of Calverton, in the County of Nottingham, Yeoman. Being by the goodness of God in some infirmity of body, though otherwise, praised be to God, of perfect mind and memory, do make this my last will and testament. In manner and form following: First and principally, I commend my soul into the hands of Almighty God, My Master and Alone Saviour, by whose precious death and blood shedding, I confidently hope to be made partaker of his everlasting kingdom.

Secondly: I commend my body to the earth whereof I become man. To be buried in the Church or Churchyard of Calverton at the discretion of my executors hereafter named.

Item: I give towards the increasing of the poor man's stock in Calverton, aforesaid . . . 7 shillings. The use thereof to be bestowed yearly as the custom is, upon Good Friday to the several relief of the poorest inhabitants there.

Item: I give to my son, John Lee that house and tenement, in Calverton, wherein I now dwell, with all and singular, the lands, meadows and closures, commodities and emoluments whatsoever . . . with the appurtenances thereto belonging. Site, lying and being within the parish and territories in Calverton aforesaid. (In manorial rolls of Calverton.)

Item: I give to John Lee, my son, one parcel of ground called Thorndall, within the Parish of Calverton, the which Thorndall is assorte, and is in the King's books 8 acres or thereabouts, by estimation, and pays to the King 6 pence yearly: Also, I give to John, my son, one other parcel of ground, within the Parish of Oxton, called the 'Myrie Meadow'. To have and to hold the said parcels of ground or closes with all the appurtenances thereto belonging, to him and his heirs forever.

Item: I give to Isabel, my daughter, wife of Robert Hathaway, 40 shillings . . . the same Robert, sealing and delivering as his deed to my executors, if it be tendered, a general release, as the payment thereof for all demands whatsoever which he, in right of his said wife might challenge or claim out of my goods instead, for and in the name of a child's part or customary portion.

And furthermore:

I give to John Lee, my son, one table and frame, with all the benches, seelings and glass, in and about my houses, with all and singular 'lyinge' houses, hovels, crathes, gates, rayles and stoops. With the pails standing and being in and upon any part of the premises in any respect. To have and enjoy the same houses with the premises, and every part and parcel thereof, to the said John, my son, his heirs and assigns forevermore.

And, whereas I, by force of a lease am possessed of my messuage and farm in Morwood, in the County of Morwood . . . by and during my actual life, and three years after my decease, the reversion only in my son Edward, as by the conveyances thereof made, it doth plainly appear I do, by this my present testament give and bequeath to Edward my son, the three years reserved to me and my assigns absolutely; upon this condition, that he, the said Edward do pay and satisfy to John Wright, my son-in-law, the sum of five pounds in full discharge of his wife's filial part or customary portion. The said John Wright a like discharge to the same effect as aforesaid, as is to be done by my son-in-law Robert Hathaway.

Item: I give to John Swift, my son-in-law, 10 shillings, and he making a like discharge as aforesaid.

Item: I give to *my eldest son, William Lee,* one ring of gold, in the value worth 20 shillings, in full discharge of his filial portion. He making the like discharge.

Item: I give to Edward my son, all those my goods, moveable and unmoveable, which shall happen to be at the said Morwood, at the time of my decease.

Item: I give to everyone of my children's children, which shall be alive at my decease, an ewe sheep of one year old at the least, and I do ordain and make my two sons, the full executor of this, my last will and testament, to whom I give the residue of all my goods, to be equally divided between them.

In witness thereof, I have set my hand and seal, these being witnesses at my request.

William Lee.   (His Mark)   X

John Lupton
Avery Pepper
John Sturtevant.

Date of Probate: June 26, 1607
Date of Will: April 16, 1607.
'Source) Nottinghamshire County Record Office DD PRSW (1607)

A TRUE INVENTORY OF ALL THE GOODS AND CHATTELS OF WILLIAM LEE, LATE OF CALVERTON, IN THE COUNTY OF NOTTINGHAMSHIRE. YEOMAN, DECEASED

Viewed and appraised by John Sturtevant, John Presswell, John Lupton and Avery Pepper. The Second day of June 1607

In the house: In Primis

His purse, girdle and his apparel	8£.	
Item: All the silings and the tables, all the forms and benches	40s.	
Item: Two chairs and their reckness, a fire-iron, one pair of tongs and a fire skounere	5s.	

In the parlour:

Item: Two bedsteads, two chests and one press	10s.	
Item: One barrel and certain garthes	5s.	4d.
Item: One mattress, one flock bed, one blanket, one bolster	13s.	4d.
Item: One press with all the other implements	3s.	4d.

In the chamber:

Item Two bedsteads, two chests	13s.	4d.
Item: Four blankets	24s.	
Item: One feather bed, one mattress and quilt, one coverlet, two pillows	38s.	
Item: Nine coverlets, two blankets, two pillows	33s.	4d.
Item: Two cushions	6s.	
Item: Three bolsters	10s.	
Item: Yarn, Tow and Wool	36s.	8d.
Two pieces of hempine	?	
Item: Two table cloathes, six pillow cases, two napkins and two towels	22s.	
Item: Nine pair of sheets	50s.	
Item: Two trestles, one plank with other implements	12d.	

In one other chamber:
Item: Wheat, rye and peas   3£. 15s.
Item: Bacon and grease   30s. 4d.
Item: One chest, shelves, tubs and all other imple-
    ments   12s.
Item: Old scythes, horse geare and beaste geare   6s. 8d.

In the kitchen:
Item: Pots, pans and kettles   46s. 8d.
Item: One iron gavelocks, hatches, axes, iron spades,
    spits, fringe pans and other implements of iron   40s.
Item: Four tubs, 2 sues, and six kittes (pais)   20s.
Item: One pair of malt querms, a pair of mustard
    querms, two chests and two stone trucks   27s.

In the nether chamber:
Item: Two servants beds with furniture to them, one
    chest, two wheels and other implements   16s.

In the milk house:
Item: All the pewter, candlesticks and spoons   20s.
Item: Earthern posts, churns, bowls, dishes and
    certain shelves and other implements   13s. 4d.

In the kiln house:
Item: All the malt   3£.
Item: One dry vat, one hair cloth, six sacks and a
    strike, with other implements   16s.
Item: Rye straw   6s.

In the yard:
Item: All the horses, colts and fillies   10£. 13s. 4d.
Item: Two iron-bound wains, and one bare wain,
    and one old wagon-body   4£.
Item: Plows, harrows, plough irons and yokes, tees,
    horse-geare, wagon ropes and other imple-
    ments   3£.
Item: Four Swine and seven pigs   30s.
Item: Hovels, hinge-houses, pales, stoops and gates,
    standing and on the ground   3£.

Item: Three stone troughs, 2 wooden troughs, one
    grind-stone   22s. 4d.
Item: All the coals, one hive with bees   18s. 8d.
Item: All the manure in the yard and the hurdles   30s.
Item: Cocks, hen and geese   10s.

In the fields:
Item: 4 ox-gangs of corn, one pea-stack, two loads
    of hay   51£. 6s.
Item: Seven score and three sheep (= 143)   42£. 18s.
Item: Four bullocks   10£. 10s.
Item: Seven kine   14£.
Item: Four young beastes (young bullocks)   9£. 3s. 4d.
Item: Three yearling calves   40s.
Item: Four young beasts   6£.
Item: Four weaning calves   26s. 8d.
                                                    _____
                              The Sum Total   203£. 14s. 8d.
                                                    _____

(Source) Wills of the Peculiar of Southwell.
         Now in County Record Office, Nottingham
         Transferred from Southwell in 1859 to
         Nottingham Probate Registry, and to C.R.O. in 1954.

CONTRACT

Between William Lee and Pierre de Caux
For a company to manufacture stockings of silk and of wool
Upon a loom to be introduced in France.
Acknowledged before the *Tabellione* of Rouen, Feb. 10, 1611

We, Pierre de Caux, a citizen of Rouen, and as far as I may obligate these honourable gentlemen, namely, Nicholas de Format, Gentleman, a resident of Carreaux, and Jacques le Tartier, a resident of Pouilly, now living in Paris, and from whom I promise to secure this document to be agreed upon and have ratified within two months from today . . . and Guillaume Lee (William Lee) an English Gentleman, at present a resident in this city of Rouen. We know and admit we have organized a company for manufacturing stockings of silk and wool, upon a loom to be presently introduced in this country, under the conditions, agreements and understandings which follow.

It is acknowledged that I, the aforesaid Lee, the inventor and chief executive of the manufacture obligated above, shall supply six English workmen, skilled in the working and operation of these machines. To this, all parties are agreed. (The names of these men are) Jehan Grangyer, and Jehan Stede (who will remain) for a period of two years, Helie Yonc for four years, Francois Fulgeaue, Andre Raynel and George Onyc, for five years. To commence on the specified time and to work at the manufacture, from after the day of the Feast of the Annunciation of Notre Dame, (March 25) Sunday of the year 1610.

I, (Lee) shall be obligated to supply four machines, in good condition, and ready for operation, besides the other four already delivered, following the first contract with the said de Caux. These first four machines having already been delivered to me, this will now make a total number of eight machines.

I agree to, and am obligated to teach, or make others to teach, as large a number of apprentices as there will be looms made, but no more. And in addition I shall be obligated to teach not only the operation of these looms, but also how to build and how to dismantle the aforesaid looms.

Similarly, I shall be obligated to instruct and to teach, one or more iron-workers the secret of manufacturing these looms and engines, without concealing anything whatsoever.

And our part, de Caux states, and in the name of M. Format and M. Le Tartier, we are associated in a joint and several obligation, without division, and we promise to pay the aforesaid Lee the repayment in full for the labour which his workers have performed for the benefit of the company, for the last four looms which they have supplied heretofore. (This will be) the sum of 2500 livres, beginning with 700 livres cash, 600 livres on the Day of the Annunciation following, and the balance in three instalments, at equal intervals of three months; with the sum each year of 100 livres, as a bonus, for Jehan Grangyer and Jehan Stede, two mechanics working in the said manufacture. And in the absence of Grangyer and Stede, 50 livres, to such other, for each one of the better mechanics, who will be named by Lee.

We agree as a joint obligation, there shall be supplied 32 additional machines, besides the 8 already provided for. This is to be done as speedily as possible.

We will also advance, loan, or provide to the aforesaid Lee, the funds that will be required for the looms and engines, provided the aforesaid associates have not had them made better themselves, otherwise they will be obligated to make the advances on their part, as will also the aforesaid Lee. They will reimburse themselves out of the profits, if the company shall fail, and not before. And in case the company should fail before the specified time (of the period of the contract) the looms will be shared between themselves and the aforesaid Lee, who in this case will be obligated to pay his part.

We agree to furnish and loan by us, de Caux and associates, all that will be necessary for the continuation of this association and operation. We will provide for the sustenance of the workers who will be compensated monthly, for the payment of the hired servants (the going rates for such help) and the rent for quarters. (Also) money for silk, wool and other materials, as well as for such other things generally used in the maintenance of the aforesaid manufacture.

Nevertheless, if the time should come when they should be without work, unproductivity, the aforesaid Lee should be exempted from making advances, or to contribute in the proportion of his ownership.

In which case, then, the parties to the contract will have an accounting of the whole affair.

A record shall be kept by each one, each week, a record of what is paid for the things aforementioned, and every three months there shall be an accounting of what has taken place, handled, sold and distributed.

For the profit and income is to be shared equally, in five or six shares, of which one share will be for Lee and the other four or five parts for the other associates. Nevertheless (when there shall be a division of profits) the said Lee shall have a part equal to that of us, the aforesaid associates.

It is agreed that in case of default, and there is not furnished by us the things aforementioned, and there shall be work stoppage, which should begin the day after the following Annunciation of Notre Dame, we shall be held responsible to pay for the benefit of the aforesaid Lee alone, the sum of 75 livres for each week of default, for the particular interest of the aforesaid Lee alone.

And if the time of three months shall have passed, from the day of the said default, and service of a writ, or a summons, shall have been made previously, upon de Caux, or any of his associates, the said Lee and his apprentices shall be free to depart from this country, without being held responsible for making any restitution, for any of the money they may have received from the sums specified above. Nor to contribute to the sending back of himself and his apprentices. The total obligation, after all, to remain, in the full loss of us, of we de Caux and associates.

The foregoing association is for the time and period of 19 years, to begin the day following the next Annunciation. With the unqualified loss or profit remaining with us alone, without the fact, that if the said Lee should be obliged to give a contribution in any way or sort possible. And if the said Lee should happen to die before the said time of 19 years is completed, the same associations will be continued with his widow, his heirs or others, for whose benefit Lee would otherwise dispose (of his estate) through a will or contract. They will be entitled to the same profit and money which would have gone to Lee.

If, nevertheless, it should be found, there would be a large loss in the conduct and continuation of the association, or if there should not be a profit, at least, in the ratio of 10 to 100, it shall be the right of each one of the association to withdraw. But it would only be from the day during which a declaration would be officially made and said. After that, the foregoing accounts should be stopped and settled.

But Lee shall be entirely free to manufacture for his own account, or to stop, as he wishes. He may carry away his apprentices, if he so prefers. And for the reason that the concession obtained from the King, under the name of 'Sieur de Carreaux' is for the period of 20 years, and warrants that those associated in the said manufacture, and the mechanics working in it would be given the rights of all Frenchmen.

We, the aforesaid de Caux and associates, will be obligated, within six months from this day, that the said Lee shall be in possession of all the privileges, and to secure for him letters of citizenship for himself and his family. These privileges would be verified, without any expense or trouble whatsoever, on his part.

Finally, Lee reserves the right of demanding to share in any profits that might be accrued, from the day of Annunciation in 1610, until the present, when the first accounting shall be made between us. Acknowledged before the *Tabelliones* of Rouen.

Feb. 10, 1611

De Caux
G. Lee
(Guillaume)

(Tabelliones)
Thos. du Bosc
Alland
Basine
Roisson

NOTE ON TRANSCRIPTION

Because of the time gap of nearly three centuries between the de Caux-Lee contract, dated from the original draft in 1611, and its transcription by the Archivist Charles de Beaurepaire in 1882, the authors sought to judge the accuracy of the transcribed copy. Their search was concerned also with having noted a change in handscript in a page in the original archival document.

On investigation there was revealed: (a) The transcribed copy offers 'an exact transcription of the original document for the first eight pages';[1] (b) In the original, consisting of eight 2/3 pages, the lower third of page 8 and the final 2/3 page 9 are penned in a script differing from the 'larger, clearer handscript of its first 8 pages'; (c) The portion in the changed handscript was appraised as 'undecipherable by anyone known in this country';[2] (d) The undecipherable portion was omitted in the transcribed copy.

In view of the fact that the de Caux-Lee contract was drawn in a period in France marked by anti-foreigner and anti-Protestant attitudes, there was a compelling reason to seek a clearance of the baffling section.

From the transcription[3] and its translation[4] given below, the conclusion derived is that the material further confirms the contract provisions with a safeguarding of the rights of Lee in his participation in the enterprise 'sans division'.

Significantly, though the page under consideration emphasizes the legal value of the trade agreement, it is drawn up in terms of its registration before the notaries Du Bosc, Allard, Moisson, and the witness, Bazire; the final ratification was yet to be fulfilled. Importantly, the promise held out for Lee was in the first paragraph of the document, '. . . We, Pierre de Caux promise . . . to have the document ratified 2 months from today'.

[1] Professor Howard B. Garey, Department of French and Romance Philology, Yale University.
[2] Professor Garey and Professor Eric C. Hicks, Department of Romance
[3] École Nationale des Chartres, Paris.
[4] Professor Eric C. Hicks and Mrs. Thérèse M. Hicks.

Last page 9 and 1/3 page 8 of Archival Original
de Caux-Lee Contract (1611)

Savoir faisons que par devant Thomas du // Bosc et Abraham
Moisson tabellions royaux a Rouen // furent presens ledit sieur de
Caux tant pour // luy et en son nom que pour et au nom et soy //
faisant fort desdits sieurs des Carreaulx et Le // Tartier dessus
nommés ausquels il a promis // faire ratiffier ces presentes comme
devant est dict d'une // part, et ledit Lee d'autre part; lesquelz //
apres qu'ilz ont recogneu avoir murement desliberé // l'association
accord et promesses dessus jurées et // desquelles la teneur ensuit,
lesdites parties isy nomées de leur bon gré et volonté ont accordé et //
consenty le tout sortira effect et execution par les termes moyens
charges clauses et conditions // susdites, et promis le tout tenir et
entretenir de // poinct en poinct sans y contrevenir en aucune //
maniere que ce soit. Sur cete minute a signé ledit // sieur de Caux
pour luy et lesdits sieurs des Carreaulx // et Tartier par insolidité sans
division biens // et heritages, et ledit Lee en son regard aussy // tous
ses biens et heritages. Presens me // Simon Bazire procureur en la
cour de Parlement de // Rouen et Jehan Allard demeurant a Rouen.

> signé: de Caux
> Lee
> du Bosc
> Bazire tesmoing
> Allard
> Moisson

Translation of Transcription
Page 9 and 1/3 page 8 of Archival Original
de Caux-Lee contract

Be it known that before Thomas du Bosc and Abraham Moisson royal scriveners at Rouen were present the said Sieur de Caux acting for himself and in his own name as well as for and in the name of and answering for the aforementioned Sieurs des Carreaulx and Le Tartier to whom he promised to ratify these presents as is stated above as party of the first part, and the said Lee as party of the second part; who after having soundly deliberated the association agreement and promises sworn above and of which the terms follow, the said parties named here freely and willingly agreed and consented the whole which effect and execution will follow by the aforementioned terms means clauses and conditions, and promised to hold and keep the whole in every article without transgression in any manner whatever. On this draft signed the said Sieur de Caux for himself and the said Sieurs des Carreaulx and Tartier without division of goods and inheritances, and the said Lee in his regard as well all his goods and inheritance. In the presence of Monseigneur Simon Bazire solicitor of the Parlement of Rouen and Jehan Allard resident of Rouen.

> *signed:* de Caux
> Lee
> Du Bosc
> Bazire witness
> Allard
> Moisson

BIBLIOGRAPHY

STATE PAPERS
Acts of Privy Council.
Statutes of the Realm.
Calendar of State Papers: Domestic Series—Reigns of Elizabeth I and James I.

RECORDS
Proceedings of Court of Aldermen, Corporation of London, Repertory 27, Folio 87.
Bridewell Hospital: *Extracts from Records and Court Books*, 1798.
Thomson Tracts E, 160 (4).
Antiquary Repertory IV 65.
Thoroton Society *Transactions*, Nottingham.
Annals of Notts, 1568–79.
Nottingham County Records.
Visitations of the County of Nottingham (1569 and 1614).
Records of the Borough of Nottingham.
Peile's *Biographical Register* (1505–1905), Christ's College, 1910.
University Archives, Grace Books Delta, The Old Schools, Cambridge University.
Records of the City of Norwich.
Norwich Court Books from 1530.
Calverton Parish Records: St. Wilfrid's Church.
Woodborough Parish Records: St. Swithin's Church.
Thoroton-Orston Parish Records: County Record Office, Nottingham.
Petition of Worshipful Company of Framework Knitters to Cromwell, 1655–1657.
Archives Départmentales, Rouen, France:
De Caux-Lee Contract: Registre des Meubles.
Registres du Tabellionage de Rouen.
Registres du Parlaiment de Normandie.
Will and Probate: William Lee, Yeoman, April 16, 1607: County Record Office, Nottingham.
Will and Probate: Margaret Oliver, January 4, 1565: County Record Office, Nottingham.
⎰ Bulletin X iii, 228: *Société de l'histoire de Protestantism Français*,
⎱ Bulletin i, 435, 441–2: *Revue d'histoire et d'archéologie*: Manuscript Division, British Museum.

MISCELLANEOUS
Book of Trades or Useful Arts, 1804.
Bulletins de la Commission des Antiquités de la Seine-Inférieure, Archives Departementales, Rouen.
Accounts of Ripon, Yorkshire: Surtees Society, 1875.
Ciba Review 106, Basle. Article *The Stocking,* A. Latour, 1954.
Dictionnaire Portatif des Arts et Métiers: Jaubert, Abbé Pierre, 1802.
Dictionnaire de Biographie Française: Libraire Letouzey.
Dictionnaire Historique des Arts: Franklin, Alfred, 1906.
Dictionnaire Universel du Commerce: Savary des Bruslons, J., 1723.
Dura Europos: *Excavations;* accounts by Yale University and French Academy of Inscriptions and Letters, 1945.
Encyclopédie Diderot. Dover Publications reprint, 1959.
Encyclopédie Méthodique, Tome I, *Arts and Métiers:* Charles Perrault.
St. John's College, *The Eagle* magazine, Vol. 15, 1889, Vol. 16, 1890.
Economic History Review: *The London Silkwoman:* M. K. Dale, October 1933.
Economica: *The Worshipful Company of Framework Knitters* (J. D. Chambers), November 1929.
Huguenot Society Publications: *Proceedings and reprints of Church Registers and Letters of Denization of Aliens.*
Revue des Sociétés Savantes, 2° semestre 5° série, XXIX, 1870.

Aikin, Lucy: *Memoirs of the Court of Elizabeth,* 1818.
Anonymous Historian of Nottingham: Thoroton Society *Annals,* Vol. II, 1898.
Arnold's *Chronicles: Customs of London,* 1811 (see Douce, Francis, infra).
Armstrong, A. J.: *History of the County of Norfolk,* 1781.
Ascham, Roger: *Letters and Works,* 1701.

Baird, Henry M.: *The Huguenots and the Revocation of the Edict of Nantes,* 1895.
Beaumont, R. M.: *The Chapter of Southwell Minster,* 1956.
Beaurepaire, Charles de: *Notes sur Salomon de Caux:* Bulletin de la Commission des Antiquités de la Seine-Inférieure, Tome VIII, Livraison 1, 1888.
    Reprint, De Caux-Lee Contract: Bulletin de la Commission des Antiquités de la Seine-Inférieure, Tome VIII, Livraison 1, 1888.
    Notes sur d'Anciennes Fabriques de Rouen d'Après des Declarations d'exportation: Bulletin de la Commission, des Antiquités de la Seine-Inférieure, Tome XIII, Livraison 3, 1888.
    Derniers Mélanges Historiques, 1892.

Beckmann, Johan: *History of Inventions*, 1789.
Bickley, F. B.: *The Little Red Book of Bristol*, 1900.
Bindoff, S. T.: *Tudor England*, 1950.
Birch, Thomas: *Memorials of the Reign of Queen Elizabeth*, 1754.
　　　　　　Life of Henry, Prince of Wales, 1760.
Blackner, John: *Histroy of Nottingham*, 1815.
Bohum, Edmund: *Character of Queen Elizabeth*, 1693.
Boissonade, P.: *Le Socialisme d'Etat* (1453–1661), 1927.
Bowen, Thomas: *Bridewell Hospital*, 1798 (see *Records* infra).
Brown, Cornelius: *History of Nottinghamshire*, 1840.
　　　　　　Lives of Nottingham Worthies, 1882.
Buckland, Rev. Walter: *History of Woodborough*, 1897.
Burgon, Thomas W.: *Life and Times of Sir Thomas Gresham*, 1839.
Burn, S. J.: *History of Foreign Protestant Refugees Settled in England*, 1846.
Burnley, James: *The Romance of Invention*, 1886.
　　　　　　Story of British Trade, 1904.

Camden, William: *Annales, The True and Royall History of the Famous Empresse Elizabeth*, 1625.
　　　　　　Brittania, 1627.
Campbell, Mildred: *The English Yeoman under Elizabeth and the early Stuarts*, 1942.
Cartwright, Edmund: *Memoirs of my Inventions*, 1843.
Chalomell, M. Augustin: *Fashions in Europe*, 1882.
Chambers, J. D.: *Nottinghamshire in the 18th Century*, 1932.
Champollian-Figeac: *Documents Historiques Inédits:* Melanges Historiques, Tome IV, 1885.
Cirket, A. F.: *English Wills*, 1957.
Clapham, Sir John: *Economic History of Britain*, 1957.
Clode, C. M.: *The Early History of the Merchant Taylors' Company*, 1888.
　　　　　　Memorials of the Gild of Merchant Taylors' Company, 1875.
Cochet, Abbé: *Galérie Dieppoise*, 1846.
Cole, Charles Wolsey: *French Mercantilist Doctrines Before Colbert*, 1931.
Collins, Arthur: *Life of William Cecil*, 1732.
Consitt, Francis: *London Weavers' Company*, 1933.
Cooper, C. H.: *Athenae Cantabrigiensis*, 1840.
　　　　　　Annals of Cambridge, 1842.
Craik and Macfarlane: *History of England*, 1846.
Cripps, Henry: *Laws of the Church and Clergy*, 1863.
Cunningham, W.: *Growth of English Industry and Commerce*, 1910 edition.

Davies, Margaret Day: *Enforcement of English Apprenticeship Laws*, 1956.
Davis, William Stearnes: *History of France*, 1910.

Davis, J.: Printer of Broadside *Memorial to Lee*, date unknown.
De Caux, Salomon: *La Perspective avec La Raison des Ombres et Miroirs*, 1612.
Deering, Charles: *Nottingham Vetus et Nova*, 1751.
Dibdin, M.: *Voyage en Normandie*. (Source: *Bibliographical, Antiquarian, and Picturesque Tour in France*, translation of T. S. Licquet, 1825.)
Dickens, A. J.: *The English Reformation*, 1965.
Ditchfield, P. H.: *The Old Time Parson*, 1905.
Douce, Francis: (see Arnold's *Chronicles*).
Dyer, George: *History of the University of Cambridge*, 1814.

Ellis, Henry: *Original Letters Illustrative of English History*, 1842 edition.
Elton, Charles: *William Shakespeare, His Family and Friends*, 1904.

Fagniez, Gustave: *L'Economie Sociale de la France sous Henri IV*, 1897.
Felkin, William: *A History of the Machine-Wrought Hosiery and Lace Manufacturers*, 1867.
Fisher, J. J.: *Studies in Economic and Social History of Tudor and Stuart England*, 1961.
Floquet, Pierre A.: *Histoire du Parlement de Normandie*, 1840.
Anecdotes Normandes, 1883.
Frère, Edouard: *Guide de Rouen*, 1843.
Froude, James: *History of England*, 1867.
Fuller, Thomas: *The History of the Worthies of England*, 1840 edition.

Gosselin, E.: *Glanes Historiques Normandes, Documents Authentiques Inédits*, 1869.
Documents sur la Marine Marchande, 1876.
Memoir Précité, 1876.
Grass, Milton N.: *History of Hosiery*, 1955.
Gunther, R. T.: *Early Science at Cambridge*, 1937.

Haag, E. and E.: *La France Protestante*, Tome III, 2nd edition, 1877.
Hakluyt, Richard: *Principal Navigations, Voyages and Discoveries of the English Nation*, 1589.
Hall, Edward: *Chronicles*, 1809 edition.
Hanotaux, Gabriel: *Histoire de la Nation Française*, Tome X, 1927.
Harrison, Rev. William: *Description of the Island of Great Britain*, 2nd edition, 1587.
Harrison, G. B.: Editor. *Letters of Queen Elizabeth*, 1935.
An Elizabethan Journal (1591–94), 1929.
Harington, Sir John: *Nugae Antiquae*, 1769.
Hauser, Henri: *Histoire de France*, Livre premier, 1925.

Heddé, M.: *Histoire de l'invention des métiers de bas:* Academie de Nîmes Proces Verbaux, 1852.

Henson, Gravener: *History of Framework Knitting and Lace Trades,* 1831.

Hermstadt: *Grundiss der Technologie* (in Chamberlain's *Knitted Footwear*), 1950

Hoare, Rev. Edward Newenham: *A Brave Fight,* 1882.

Holinshed, Raphael: *Chronicles,* 1607 (also editions of 1577 and 1808).

Homer: *The Iliad* (Arthur Cullen Bryant's translation).

Horrocks, J. W.: *A Short History of Mercantilism,* 1925.

Hoskins, W. G.: *Essays in Leicestershire History,* 1950.

Howell, Dr.: *History of the World,* 1670.

Isaacson, E.: *Life and Death of Andrewes,* 1650.

Jenkins, Elizabeth: *Elizabeth the Great,* 1959.
        Elizabeth and Leicester, 1962.
Johnson, Rev. A. H.: *History of the Worshipful Company of Drapers of London,* 1914.

Laffemes, Barthelèmy de: *Reiglement Générale Pour Dresser les Manufactures,* 1601.

Lambarde, E. M.: *Perambulations of Kent,* 1576.

Le Blanc, M. V.: *Manuel du Bonnetier et du Fabricant de Bas,* 1830.

Le Gendre, P.: *Historie de la Persecution faite à l'Eglise de Rouen,* 1874.

Leonard, E. M.: *Early History of English Poor Relief,* 1900.

Lesens, M.: *Le Protestant dans le pays de Caux,* 1906.

Lipson, E.: *The Economic History of England,* Vol. I, 12th edition, 1959.

Lydgate, John: *London Lickpenny* (1370–1451) in Percy Society *Early English Poetry,* 1842.

Machiavelli, Nicolo: *The Prince,* 1500.

MacPherson, David: *Annals of Commerce,* Vol. II, 1805.

Maks, Christina Sandrena: *Salomon de Caux, Le Fameux Ingénieur, Architecte et Musicien,* 1935.

Mellors, Robert: *Nottingham Then and Now,* 1914.

Melville, Sir James: *Memoirs,* 1630.

Mezeray, François de: *Histoire de France,* 1692.

Mirsky and Nevins: *The World of Eli Whitney,* 1952.

Mitchell, R. J., and M. D. R. Leys: *History of the English People,* 1950.

Moens, W. J. C.: *The Walloons and their Church at Norwich,* Vol. I, Huguenot Society Publications.

Moryson, Fynes: *Itinerary*, 1617.
Mullinger, J. B.: *University of Cambridge from* 1535 *to the Accession of Charles II*, 1884.
Myers, John: *Primitive Man in Geologic Times*, Cambridge Ancient History, 1923 edition.

Naunton, Sir Robert: *Fragmenta Regalia, Observations on the Late Queen Elizabeth*, 1653.
Neale, J. E.: *The Age of Catherine de Medici and Essays in Elizabethan History*, 1963.
　　Queen Elizabeth, 1934.
　　Elizabeth I and Her Parliaments, 1953.
Nef, John U.: *Industry and Government in France and England* (1540–1640), 1940.
Nichols, John: *Progresses and Public Processions of Queen Elizabeth*, 1708.
　　History and Antiquities of the County of Leicester, 1811 edition.
　　Illustrations of the Manners and Expenses of Ancient Times in England, with explanatory notes by J.N., 1797.
Norris, Herbert: *Costume and Fashion*, 1938.

Orange, James: *History of Nottingham*, 1840.
Ouin-Lactoix, M. L'Abbé: *Histoire des Anciennes Corporations de Rouen, d'arts et métiers et des Confrères Religieuses de la Capitale de la Normandie*, 1850.
Oursel, N. N.: *Nouvelle Biographiee Normande*, 1886.

Paget and Irvine: *History of Leicester*, 1955.
Pannier, J.: *L'Église Reformée de Paris sous Henri IV*, 1911.
Peacham, Henry: *The Compleat Gentleman*, 1634.
Peck, Francis: *Desiderata Curiosa*, 1779.
Peile, J.: *Christ's College*, 1900.
Perkins, William: *Workes, or, A Golden Chaine*, 1591.
　　A Treatise of the Vocations, 1603.
Petrie, Sir W. M. Flinders: *Hawara, Biahmu and Stinoe*, 1889.
Peyton, S. A.: *The Village Population in The Tudor Lay Subsidy Rolls*, 1915.
Pickering, A. J.: *Cradle and Home of the Hosiery Trade*, 1940.
Porter, H. C.: *Aspects of Religious Life and Thought in the University of Cambridge* (1500–1650), 1958.
Price, W. H.: *The English Patents of Monopoly*, 1906.

Quickerat, Jules: *Histoire du Costume en France*, 1875.

Read, Conyers: *Mr. Secretary Walsingham and the Policy of Queen Elizabeth*, 1955.
　　Mr. Secretary Cecil and Queen Elizabeth, 1955.
　　Lord Burghley and Queen Elizabeth, 1960.
Renouard, Alfred: *Traité complet de Bonneterie Mécanique*, 1921.
Rowlett, W. T.: *Technology of Framework Knitting*, 1884 (translated from the original work of Gustav Wilkomm).
Rowse, A. L.: *The England of Elizabeth*, 1950.
　　The Expansion of Elizabethan England, 1955.
　　The Elizabethans and America, 1959.
　　William Shakespeare, 1963.
Ryan, E. K. W.: *A Short History of Cripplegate, Finsbury and Moorfields*, 1817.

Salzman, L. F.: *English Trade in the Middle Ages*, 1931.
Schmidt, Albert J.: *The Yeoman in Tudor and Stuart England*, 1961.
Scouloudi, Irene: *Immigration and Alien Communities in London* (1558–1640) (unpublished thesis), 1936.
Seymour: *Survey of London*, 1734.
Singer, Charles J.: *History of Technology*, 1954.
Sitwell, Edith: *The Queens and the Hive*, 1962.
Smiles, Samuel: *The Huguenots, Their Settlement, Churches, and Industry in England*, 1868.
Smith, Rev. T. W.: *Papers relative to Tercentenary of William Lee*, 1888.
Speed, John: *Atlas of England and Wales*, 1677.
Spenser, Edmund: *Mother Hubbard's Tale*, 1603.
Stevenson, W. H.: *Records of Nottingham*, 1882.
Stow, John: *The Annales, or General Chronicles of England*, 1615.
　　Survey of London, 1630.
Strype, John: *Annals of the Reformation*, 1824.
　　Historical and Biographical Works, editions of 1812–1824.
Stubbes, Philip: *Anatomie of Abuses*, 1583.
Sully, Maximilian, Duc de: *Memoirs*, 1856.

Tawney, R. H.: *Religion and the Rise of Capitalism*, 1926.
Tawney, R. H. and Power, E.: *Tudor Economic Documents*, 1924.
Taylor, E. G. R.: *Tudor Geography* (1485–1583), 1931.
Théry, Georges: *Recueil des Actes de la Vénérable Marie Poussepin* Tome I, *Période de Dourdan*, 1938.
Thirsk, Joan: *The Rise in Rural Industries* (1550–1560), 1961. (see J. J. Fisher infra.)
Thompson, Craig R.: *Universities in Tudor England*, 1959.
　　The English Church in the 16th Century, 1958.

Thorndyke, Ashley H.: *Shakespeare's Theatre*, 1916.
Thoroton, Robert: *Antiquities of Nottinghamshire*, 1677.
Throsby, John: *History and Antiquities, Town of Nottingham*, 1795.
Timbes, John, *Stories of Inventors and Discoverers*, 1860.
Trevelyan, G. M.: *History of England*, Vol II, 1953 edition.
                 English Social History, 1944.
Tusser, T.: *Five Hundred Points of Good Husbandrie*, 1557.

Ude, Georges: *Etude Générale de la Bonneterie*, 1930.
Udall, Nicholas: *Ralph Roister Doister*, 1534
Unwin, George: *Industrial Organization in the 16th and 17th Centuries,*
                 1904.
                 The Gilds and Companies of London, 1938.
Usher, Albert Payson: *A History of Mechanical Inventors*, 1954.

Victoria Histories of the Counties of England: *Nottinghamshire, Leicestershire,*
                 Suffolk and Norfolk.
Vitet, L.: *Histoire de Dieppe*, 1844.
Voyages of Marco Polo, Yule Edition.

Waller, W. C.: *Extracts from the Court Book of the Weavers' Company*, 1931.
Walpole, Horace: *Letters and Essays*, 1798.
Welles, F. A.: *The British Hosiery Trade*, 1935.
Wilson, Thomas: *The Art of Rhetoric*, 1560.
Wolff and Mauro: *Histoire Générale du Travail*—Nouvelle Librarie de
                 France, 1961.
Wood, Alfred C.: *Nottinghamshire in the Civil Wars*, 1937.
                 History of Trade and Transport on the River Trent (see
                 Annals—Thoroton Society, Vol. LIV., 1950).
                 A History of Nottinghamshire, 1947.
Wood, Norman: *The Reformation and English Education*, 1934.
Woodman, J. F. U.: *Freedom of the City*, 1960.
Woodward, G. W. *Short History of the 16th Century, England (1485–1603)*,
                 1963.
Wright, Louis B.: *Middle Class Culture in Elizabethan England*, 1935.
                 Religion and Empire: The Alliance between Poverty and
                 Commerce, 1943.
Wylie, Wm. H.: *Old and New Nottingham*, 1853.

INDEX